BLAGO BUNG BLAGO BUNG BOSSO FATAKA!

GW00758794

BLAGO BUNG

BLAGO BUNG

Bosso Fataka!

FIRST TEXTS OF GERMAN DADA BY

HUGO BALL

RICHARD HUELSENBECK

WALTER SERNER

Translated & Introduced by

Malcolm Green

Published By Atlas Press
BCM ATLAS PRESS, LONDON WCIN 3XX
© 1995, Atlas Press
All English language rights reserved
English language translation © 1995 Malcolm Green.
German texts: Richard Huelsenbeck, *Phantastische Gebete* © 1960 Verlags AG die Arche,
Zurich; Hugo Ball, *Tenderenda der Phantast* by kind permission of Mrs F. Hauswirth; Walter
Serner, *Letzte Lockerung manifest* © 1982 Verlag Klaus G. Renner, Munich.
Printed by The Bath Press, UK.
A CIP record for this book is available from The British Library.
ISBN 0 947757 86 4
Special thanks to Thomas Milch for his help.

Funded by
THE
ARTS
COUNCIL
OF ENGLAND

R I C H A R D ■ H U E L S E N B E C K ■ F A N T A S T I C ■ P R A Y E R S

This collection presents, for the first time in English, three pivotal Dada publications: the first collection of Dada poems in any language, *the* Dada novel, and the single most important Dada manifesto published during the movement's heyday in Zurich. Not only are they among the fiercest productions of one of the most turbulent cultural movements of our epoch, but all three texts can be seen as the authors' single most important works, the ones which they worked on, revised, republished, or kept returning to over the longest periods of time.

In May 1915, the writer Hugo Ball arrived in Switzerland with his future wife, Emmy Hennings, in order to escape Germany and the war and accept an invitation to collaborate on the literary journal *Der Mistral*, which was co-edited by Walter Serner, whom he had met in Berlin. The collaboration did not work out, but during the following months, while Hennings and Ball toured the provinces singing and playing piano for a small variety troupe, Ball edited an anthology of avant-garde art, poems and prose, which was later to become the first Dada publi-

cation, and conceived the idea of opening an artistic cabaret. The result was the *Cabaret Voltaire* which opened on 5 February 1916; and within a few months Ball, his comrade-in-arms from Germany, Richard Huelsenbeck, and such illustrious names as Tristan Tzara, Hans Arp, Marcel Janco et al. had dubbed their new venture *Dada*, a name that still inspires scorn, enthusiasm, bewilderment, amusement, but above all misunderstanding (which, of course, the members of the group did their utmost to foster).

Developments at the Cabaret Voltaire were rapid and exultant. New works and new techniques were conceived at a fast pace in close collaboration, and reading the protagonists' reports and diaries, it is difficult not to wonder at how so much was achieved and turned on its head in so short a time. This impression is only reinforced by the rather unassuming announcement that was inserted in the Zurich newspapers before the Cabaret's inauguration:

Cabaret Voltaire. Under this name a group of young artists and writers has been formed with the aim of creating a centre for artistic entertainment. The idea of the cabaret is that visiting artists will hold musical recitals and readings at the daily meetings. To this end we invite the young artists of Zurich, regardless of their artistic directions, to come with their suggestions and contributions.

There is little hint here of the outrages and public barrackings that characterised Dada, of the enormous creative potential that was unleashed and that produced, amongst others, the texts in this anthology: some of the fiercest ammunition fired at the audiences during the Dada performance evenings. However, all three of the texts printed here had their origins before the birth of Dada itself, and before looking at them in detail, it is useful to examine the meetings, streams of thought and influences which went into their making, and into Ball's underlying concept of Dada as a synthesis of the arts, an idea which he developed prior to the announcement above, in order to show that the Cabaret did not simply descend on war-torn Europe as a Dadaist *Deus ex machina*.[1]

When the twenty-six year-old Hugo Ball met the medical student Richard Huelsenbeck in a literary café in Munich in 1912, it was the beginning of many years of friendship and close collaboration that climaxed with the birth of Dada. Ball, who had previously studied German literature, history and philosophy and then play-direction in Munich and Berlin, was working as a literary adviser to a progressive theatre, the *Münchener Lustspielhaus*, and was already moving in the Expressionist circles into which he introduced Huelsenbeck. The new movement, still a heterogeneous mixture of

youthful defiance, late Symbolism, extreme disgust with Prussian society, was plagued by feelings of ego-dissociation and a wish to revitalise language, and had yet to concretise its calls for a 'New Man' and the hard-edged, impassioned style with which it was ultimately to become associated during and after the First World War. Many of the writers whom Ball and Huelsenbeck were to befriend, and whose works were later to be read at the Cabaret

Voltaire, exhibited a blend of metaphysical humour, dandyish hauteur and schoolboy absurdity in their writings and bearing. Furthermore it is certainly no coincidence that Ball includes concealed references in his novel *Tenderenda* to such Expressionist writers as Gottfried Benn, Carl Einstein, Else Lasker-Schüler, Jakob van Hoddis, Albert Ehrenstein and Hans Leybold, who exemplified these characteristics. Nor too, that Huelsenbeck appropriates the title of one of the most famous Expressionist poems of the period, Jakob van Hoddis' dark, absurd *The End of the World*, for one of his *Fantastic Prayers*, or that Walter Serner, who, as we shall see, came late to Dada, should keep the company of Expressionist writers while in exile in Zurich. Dada is often referred to in the German context as some sort of extremist wing[2] or absurdist offshoot of Expressionism, a notion that has a certain amount of truth provided one specifies *early* Expressionism.

In pre-war Munich and Berlin, Ball and Huelsenbeck had been champions of the Expressionist movement. Ball planned an Expressionist theatre, in part with Huelsenbeck, and the two of them contributed poems, articles and novellas to the politically forthright *Die Aktion*, one of the foremost periodicals of the movement, while Ball helped found and edit the Munich based magazine *Revolution*. Aimed more at a literary revolution than a political one, the periodical was however consciously directed at demoralising the bourgeois, with its emphasis on sexual liberation, internationalism (Huelsenbeck was its 'Paris correspondent' without ever having visited the city) and its sometimes proto-Dadaist assaults on meaning and intelligence. This magazine not only brought Ball into the public eye for the first time as a result of his poem *The Hangman*, which contained several highly provocative lines about the Virgin Mary – this issue of the magazine was impounded and Ball was arraigned for obscenity – but also initiated another important collaboration, this time with its editor, Hans Leybold.

Their mutual interests – theatre, Expressionism (it was Leybold who, despite being six years younger, first introduced Ball to the Expressionists), idealistic anarchism, an arrogant dandyism, and the "cultivating of poses, gestures and vexation" (according to Ball's obituary of Leybold, 1915) – led quickly to a deep friendship, which in turn produced a remarkable

series of poems which they wrote together under the name Ha Hu Baley (taken from the first syllables of their names), and published in *Die Aktion*. These poems are among the clearest precursors of Dada that can be found in literary Expressionism. Not only do we find lines like: "A double-decker climbs out of every bottle/and beats in its head with a wail," but also the theme of the '*rasta*' (from the French *rastaquouère*, a low-life swindler or adventurer) so beloved of the Dadaists. Leybold even wrote an article for *Revolution* on the use of 'the bluff' in art, thus anticipating one of Dada's most celebrated weapons by several years. The importance of this collaboration and friendship is often evident in Ball's novel *Tenderenda*, as for instance in his paraphrases of lines from their poems, or in the funeral oration in the chapter *Bulbo's Prayer*, in which Ball is clearly referring to his obituary of Leybold, who died at the front in 1915.

This obituary, an important precursor of Dada provocations, was read at the 'Memorial Reading for Fallen Poets' organised by Ball and Huelsenbeck in February 1915 when they returned to Berlin, sickened by their experiences of the 'Great War' (for which they had volunteered). This reading, along with two more staged that year by Ball and Huelsenbeck, and later with Emmy Hennings, established many of the aggressive and performative elements that they were later to employ in Zurich. Beside more conventional contributions from others, Huelsenbeck gave a talk on the French poet Charles Péguy, which incensed the audience on account of its undesired internationalism, after which Ball read his obituary of Leybold in a harsh, unsentimental, scornful manner that shocked the audience and created the paradoxical impression that he was actually making fun of the deceased. Both of them used the occasion

PROGRAMM
zur
Gedächtnisfeier für gefallene Dichter veranstaltet
von Hugo Ball und Richard Huelsenbeck am
Freitag, den 12. Februar 1915
abends 8¹/₂ Uhr im Architektenhaus.

Hugo Ball: Eröffnung.
A. R. Meyer: über Ernst Stadler.
Dr. Kurt Hiller: über Ernst Wilhelm Lotz.
Frau Reß Canger (Rezitation):
     Verse von Ernst Stadler, Ernst Wilhelm Lotz und
     Walter Heymann.
Hugo Ball: über Hans Leybold.
Richard Huelsenbeck: über Charles Péguy.
Frau Reß Canger (Rezitation):
     Verse von Hans Leybold,
     Prosa von Charles Péguy.

———— Preis 30 Pfennig. ————

to sling mud at establishment writers, both stood out by their aggression, arrogance and aura of intellectual superiority, and to round off the impression of Dada in the making, they handed out a manifesto full of such sentences as: "We want to provoke, perturb, bewilder, tease, tickle to death, confuse, without any context. Be reckless, negators," and "We propagate metabolism, break-neck somersaults, vampirism and all forms of mimicry." The manifesto was already assuming the scandalous 'literary form in its own right' which was to be perfected by Dada: a memorial wreath laid at the feet of language and style.

The last of these evenings, held under the banner of Expressionism, again showed the direction in which the future Dadaists were taking the movement. Huelsenbeck read 'Negro' poetry ("Umba Umba . . . the negroes dance on the raffia mattresses") which clearly contained the seeds of his *Fantastic Prayers*, and Ball's poems ("A tired horse makes itself comfy in a bird's nest") resemble lines of the novel *Tenderenda* which he had begun that year. The evening was greeted with cat-calls, laughter and confusion, and even led to a fight in the audience. One newspaper commented: "Basically it was a protest against Germany in favour

of Marinetti," and it is true that Marinetti's Futurism, despite its positivist and militarist messages, was an important influence, if only for its avant-gardism, its desire to shock and its emphasis on the performative. One of Huelsenbeck's *Fantastic Prayers* – which in general show a conscious debt to the Futurist *Parole Libre* – is called *Mafarka*, the eponymous hero of Marinetti's novel, and doubtless Ball's knowledge of Futurism provided an important reference point when he teamed up with the non-Expressionist co-founders of Dada: Tzara and Janco. But the influence of Futurism should not be overrated: in his diary, *Flight out of Time*,[3] Ball cites the newspaper comment given above, and adds: "No, it was a farewell." In answer to the call from Walter Serner, Ball had bidden farewell to Germany.

Before returning to the Cabaret Voltaire, it is important to look briefly at two other influences which were vital precursors to that newspaper

DIE FLUCHT
AUS DER ZEIT
VON
HUGO BALL.

Proximus ero, potentia fronteant
entis Oigid tinera fronit tone, quam
signo travris armant.
Augustinus.

MÜNCHEN UND LEIPZIG / 1927
VERLAG VON DUNCKER & HUMBLOT

announcement: Wassily Kandinsky, whom Ball met in Munich in 1914, and the writer and art critic Carl Einstein.

Kandinsky, a founder member of the Expressionist art group *Der Blauer Reiter* in Munich, "rejected all representation as impure and returned to the true form, the sound of things, their essence, their intrinsic being" (Ball's *Diary*), a preoccupation which was to distinguish the more mystical side of Dada, as exemplified by Ball and Arp. As a painter, writer and theoretician, Kandinsky envisaged the marriage of all artistic disciplines in a theatrical *gesamtkunstwerk* that would bring about the rebirth of art and society. This catalysed a desire in Hugo Ball the theatre director to go even further, to create a total theatre combining dance, painting and poetry, and employing stilts, megaphones etc.: a choreographed spectacle that would be an end in itself, freed of any tendentiousness, and a magical return to a state of infantilism which would overthrow rationality completely, break in upon the unconscious, and initiate change on the human rather than societal level. Ball's plans to create an Expressionist theatre were thwarted by the war, but the *Galerie Dada* evenings in May 1917, where dancers in abstract masks made by Arp and Janco performed to his sound poems, must have been close to this vision: "The dance has become an end in itself," he wrote in his diary, echoing Kandinsky's desire for pure expression and abstraction.

Kandinsky had influenced Dada in various ways (as well as his ideas on theatre, his introduction of abstraction in painting, which was important to Arp and subsequently to much of Dada; and his poetic theatre texts, which also impressed Arp and in all likelihood inspired both Ball and Huel-senbeck), and likewise Carl Einstein was also important on several accounts.

In a 'Cubist' novella entitled *Bebuquin, the Dilettantes of the Won-*

drous published in 1912,[4] Einstein produced an autonomous narrative form which called into question the survival of the psychological or realistic novel and its use of metaphor and other rhetorical devices. Set against an aphoristic collage of events, his characters, each a kaleidoscope of alternative egos, search in vain for a unity of experience and thought, but are forced in the end to follow their own mental logic to its illogical ends. This fabulous, glittering intellectual world of allusions and artifice opened the way for a "literature for discriminating bachelors," as Einstein put it,[5] an absolute, imaginative literature void of causality, associations and explanation which demonstrated that ultimately the intellect can be no more than its own aesthetic riddle.

Ball noted in his diary at the end of 1914: "Carl Einstein's *Dilettantes of the Wondrous* shows the way," and his own *Tenderenda*, aimed at creating "a

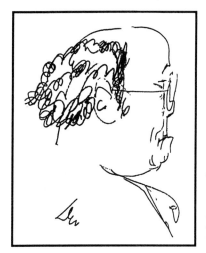

magical-archaic world, a lawless and thus enchanted world verging on absurdity," is clearly very much in Einstein's tradition, a tradition which also had another, dandyish, proto-Dadaist element of which he had already been strongly aware during his collaboration with Leybold: "Being arrogant – like Einstein."[6]

The other main influence on Dada which can be attributed to Einstein is primitivism. It would be wrong to say that the Dadaists' interest in primitivism came solely from Einstein, since the art theorist Wilhelm Worringer had already hailed primitive art in his book *Abstraction and Empathy* in 1907. The Dadaists were not the only people to be attracted to the ideas promulgated in Einstein's book *Negro Art* (1915): that African and Oceanic sculptures and carvings constituted an abstract, conceptual art and a form of direct expression free of mimesis, or the demands of optical veracity, and as such could be seen as models for the new art. The Cubists had already made much of these theories, and a notion of positive Barbarism can be identified among the early Expressionists. But the Dadaists saw in primitivism – which was characterised for them by reduction and abstraction as well as deliberate childishness – a kind of (urban) noble savage approach to escaping the mire of civilisation. They performed negro dances and music, Tzara recited negro poems, and Huelsenbeck boomed out 'primitive' rhythms on a drum at the Cabaret Voltaire while reciting his poems. The rhythms already intrinsic to the poems he read at the Expressionist Evening in Berlin are eloquent testimony to the importance of primitivism, and Ball, in a letter dated 7/10/1916, wrote "my idea of Dadaism [is] absolute negroism, in keeping with the primitive adventures of our times."

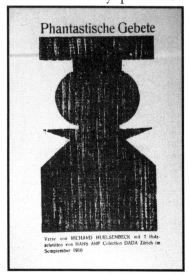

Phantastische Gebete

Verse von RICHARD HUELSENBECK mit 7 Holz-schnitten von HANS ARP Colection DADA Zürich im Semptember 1916

In all of these manifestations, the Dadaists

were intent on allowing music, movement and above all language to become 'autonomous,' in the latter case by stripping it of its normal contextual constraints so that it could establish a direct relationship once more with surrounding reality and incorporate the cacophony of life itself: such was the intention of Huelsenbeck's Bruitist[7] poems, the *Fantastic Prayers*.

Huelsenbeck wrote of them in *Dada Siegt!* (1920), that they are "the first examples in the German language of what are known in the circles of Max Jacob and Apollinaire as *vers libre*, but within each line, unconnected by any rhythmic or mental synthesis, the words remain unique spherical forms, tiny worlds with their own laws and life. Newspaper headlines and announcements run through the text, having the same function as alien

material in painting, providing a direct return to reality and the representation of the *bruit*, the squeal of brakes, which assaults the person sunk in melodies and delivers a hefty kick to the good citizen's broad backside. For the first time in the German language the *Fantastic Prayers* extol the unscrupulous colourfulness of life, they take life as it is – a crazed simultaneous concert of murder, cultural deceit, eroticism and roast pork, they decimate ethics and the lie of personal responsibility, they dissolve life in a peal of laughter by denouncing the intellect as an act of mental suppression by those with weak muscles."

In their most extreme form the *Lautgedichte* (sound poems) written and recited by Ball and included in *Tenderenda* (pages 137 & 145 below), are experiments consisting of a retirement "to the inner alchemy of the word . . . and thus retain poetry's holiest domain," a programme that will become clearer when we turn to *Tenderenda*.

So, many of the features that distinguished Dada – abstractionism, primitivism, provocation, bluffs, arrogance, dandyish absurdism and assaults on meaning and language – had a longer history than might initially be supposed. Dada was born in an amosphere of experiment and experience, not least among the other members of the Cabaret Voltaire whom I have not touched upon: Tzara and the brothers Janco were already steeped in a late Symbolism that had been turned on its head by Futurism; Arp had been involved in the Expressionist group *Die Blauer Reiter* in Munich and had co-founded the first abstract

art group in Zurich, *Der Moderne Bund*, and the chanteuse and writer Emmy Hennings had the stage charisma the cabaret required. The group was a volatile mix which simply needed the right time and place to explode, with Ball as its fuse.

The actual atmosphere of the Cabaret – bordering rather on low vaudeville (a final source of inspiration to be mentioned), which Ball and Hennings brought with them from their work in Variety – has been described at length elsewhere.[8] It is relevant to this anthology that Ball read excerpts from *Tenderenda* at the Cabaret, such as *The Decline and Fall of Swaggerprance*, *The Prophet's Ascent* and the sound poems, and Huelsenbeck's *Fantastic Prayers*, published in September 1916 as the third publication of the *Collection Dada*,[9] were a star turn at the Cabaret, while the fact that they

were written to be performed permits several interesting insights.

Of all the many monocled Dadaists in Zurich and elsewhere, Huelsenbeck was the one who most convincingly assumed the requisite pose of lofty arrogance while reading his poems. He further accompanied his recitals with two other symbols of 'civilisation,' a rosewood cane which he flailed in front of his audience in time to the rhythm, and a large military bass drum used to best Bruitist effect. "He delivered his poems as if they were insults," wrote Marcel Janco later, and Ball described him in his diary: "He comes across as arrogant and looks the part. His nostrils quiver, his eyebrows arch. An ironic sneer plays across his lips, his mouth is weary but resolute. And he reads, accompanied by the big drum, roars, whistles and laughs. . . His verses are an attempt to capture in a lucid melody the totality of these unspeakable times, with all its cracks and tears, all its din and mindless racket. The Gorgon head of a measureless horror smiles up from all this fantastic destruction."

The *Fantastic Prayers* were very much poems to be performed, as were Ball's soundpoems, but as Herbert Kapfer points out,[10] it is unlikely that Huelsenbeck strayed very far from his written texts in his readings: he was keenly aware of his personal literary aspirations, and moreover he knew his audience – the smug Zurich citizens – very well, so that it may be assumed that the poems, as printed, were already sufficiently well planned and calculated to achieve their provocative aims. In reading the poems we become aware that they are carefully sculpted to this end, attacking by turn the Church, the literary pantheon of Goethe, Schiller, Horace and Homer (who are all quoted), the patriarchal fatherland and its politics, while simultaneously paying

Phantastische Gebete

VERSE VON
RICHARD
HUELSENBECK

ZEICHNUNGEN VON
GEORGE GROSZ

DER MALIK-VERLAG/BERLIN, ABTEILUNG DADA

homage to the works of the Expressionists that Huelsenbeck and his Dada colleagues admired: Jakob van Hoddis and Alfred Lichtenstein, as well as those of the Futurist Marinetti. More intriguingly we also find words and phrases that seem to have escaped from Ball's *Tenderenda* (an enigmatic "tailbone oxy-hydrogen blowpipe," for instance, or corpses dancing around a forehead), or the poems of Hans Arp. This can be explained, as Kapfer points out, by the close collaboration within the Cabaret Voltaire group, and Ball himself drew attention to this in his diary (15/6/1916): "Huelsenbeck comes to write his latest poems on my typewriter. At every other word he turns and asks: 'or was that from you?' " then adding: "Two thirds of the wonderfully plaintive words . . . come from ancient magical texts. The way we both write is characterised by the use of 'sigils,' flying words and sound figures filled with magic. When successful, these word creations bore irresistibly and effortlessly into one's mind with hypnotic power, only to re-surface just as irresistibly and effortlessly . . .

Huelsenbeck's idolatrous prayers and several chapters of my novel have just this effect."

The Dada explosion did not, however, appeal to all of the "young artists of Zurich, regardless of their artistic directions," whom Ball invited to participate in the Cabaret Voltaire. Walter Serner – a doctor of law who had fled from Berlin to Switzerland in February 1915 after misusing his professional status to write a medical certificate for the Expressionist/later

Dadaist Franz Jung after the latter had deserted – visited the Cabaret sporadically, but was singularly unimpressed. According to his close friend Christian Schad,[11] "it seemed to him impossible even to approach the mire of deeply-rooted intellectualism by means of absurd, riotous things and then to repeat them. Or, by these means, to make new ideas viable without robbing them of their spontaneity. Although amusing at first, he saw that it would quickly become flat and fade."

In fact, Serner openly attacked Ball and Huelsenbeck in an article in his magazine *Sirius* in March 1916. Criticising them for their "unforgivable blasphemy against the intellect," he added: "They no longer believe in the intellect and its words . . . and all they produce are monkey-tricks. And if they were asked why they do it, probably they would answer that it would

be impious to expect them even to know. And they would underline their answer with a smile and this smile with a gesture of superiority." Curiously, Serner's comments refer *not* to Cabaret Voltaire, but to the manifesto which Ball and Huelsenbeck handed out at their 'Memorial Reading for Fallen Poets' in February 1915, a copy of which they had sent to the editors of *Der Mistral*, a magazine on which Serner collaborated, in the hope of establishing contact. Presumably Serner recognised in it the same spirit that was walking the boards of the Cabaret. The Dadaists did not respond, but an entry in Ball's diary can be taken as typical of the Dadaists' dim view of the commodity Serner was still championing at this time: "A plethora of intellect abounds at present, especially in Switzerland. . . We now have intellectual trouser braces, intellectual shirt buttons, the magazines brim over with intellect and the art reviews compete with one another in their intellectuality."

The gulf between Serner and the Dadaists was initially large, despite the fact that Serner had been instrumental in bringing Ball to Zurich, had known Huelsenbeck in Berlin and Arp through his collaboration on *Sirius*, and the Dadaists as a whole through many mutual acquaintances among the exiled writers and artists who populated the cafés of Zurich – and the breadth of the avant-garde that Serner presented in *Sirius* must surely have appealed to Ball, who wished from Dada a "fusion of all regenerative ideas." Serner, who in 1912 had flatly rejected modern art, above all

Cubism, as a false development in which technique and formalism overcame the artist's personality, still propounded the idea of a universally valid aesthetics. The following year and a half saw no rapprochements, and indeed few signs of life from Serner. *Sirius* folded in May 1916, and his only publication before the *Last Loosening Manifesto* included here was a foreword to the catalogue to Christian Schad's exhibition in July 1917, in which however there are signs of a change in his opinions: he shifts his previous aesthetic standpoint, which underlined the importance of style in art, away from having any universal value to a purely personal one. The nihilism which so strongly marks his *Last Loosening Manifesto* was yet to come; but even so it had been bubbling under for some time. Preliminary sketches later incorporated into the manifesto can be found in his 1915 essay *Boredom and War* in *Der Mistral*, as well as in articles in *Sirius*. Contemporary witnesses note that much of his renowned café repartee during these years was made up of aphorisms later included in the manifesto.

Serner's actual move to Dada is hard to reconstruct, being dated variously as 1917 or even as late as 1918/19.[12] When Serner took this step, whether in late 1917 or over a year later, it was during a lull in Dada's public performances. The Cabaret Voltaire closed in the summer of 1916, after just five months, and Ball split with the group. The short-lived *Galerie Dada* opened in early 1917, and Ball returned briefly, reciting soundpoems and excerpts from *Tenderenda* (such as *Grand Hotel Metaphysics*, performed in fantastic attire), but during the ensuing period the Dadaists, with Tzara now firmly at the helm, directed their energies towards broadening their international contacts and their publications, in particular Tzara's magazine *Dada*. But a definitive change occurred in the movement between late 1917 and the demise of Zurich Dada in 1919, during which the influence of Serner, who brought considerable intellectual clout to the group, and of Francis Picabia's visits, cannot be underestimated. Dada became subversive. Arp, Tzara and Serner co-wrote several poems under the collective title 'The Society for exploiting Dada language' and, more importantly, a fake press release about a duel between Tzara and Arp (cf. *Dada Almanac*, p. 34).

The group embarked on a campaign of deliberate mystification, a strategy which Serner was to perfect with dozens of skilfully placed anonymous fake newspaper articles; the group's style changed radically, as evinced by the chaotic typography of *Dada* 3 and the underlying violence of Tzara's *Manifesto Dada 1918*, and later the sheer nihilism of his *Mr. Antipyrine* cycle. And with the first and last public evening mounted by the Zurich Dadaists in the *Kaufleuten Saal*

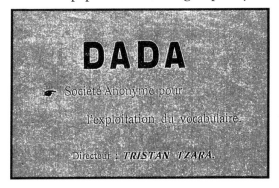

9 April 1919, the synthesis of the arts achieved in the closed performances at the Galerie Dada gave way to public outcry and scandal.

Although only Tzara and Hans Richter remained from the earlier group, some 1000 people packed the auditorium to delight in the simultaneous poems and other Dada antics. By all accounts this was politely received until Serner delivered his *Last Loosening Manifesto*: "Serner takes the floor," wrote Tristan Tzara in his *Zurich Chronicle* "to illuminate his dadaist MANIFESTO. And now, when 'a queen is an armchair a dog is a hammock' the unleashing of the tempestuous storm dizzying siren whistles bombardment song the battle breaks out in earnest, half the audience applaud the protesters hold the hall in the lungs nerves liquefy muscles jump Serner makes mocking gestures, schticks the scandal in his buttonhole / ferocity that wrings the neck / Interruption. Torn up chairs projectiles crack intended effect atrocious and instinctive." The same evening Serner, with Dadaist *sang-froid*, whipped up the audience into a second frenzy by "refusing to read his 'own poems,' as was announced in the programme . . . but instead pulled a black, headless dressmaker's dummy on stage, offered it a bouquet of roses to smell and then placed them at its wooden feet . . . a scandal the likes of which one old

Zuricher claimed he could not remember ever having witnessed," as Serner himself wrote in an anonymous article in a Swiss newspaper. Dada, in the form of Serner's nihilism, had achieved its full power to shock – which indirectly contributed to its final collapse.

It would be incorrect to say that Serner's *Last Loosening Manifesto* was the first such: it postdates Richard Huelsenbeck's polemic *Declamation* read in early 1916 at the Cabaret Voltaire, Ball's *First Dadaist Manifesto* – a deeply ironic text that was a thinly veiled farewell to Dada, read shortly before leaving the movement in the summer of 1916 – and it was published after Huelsenbeck's *Dadaist Manifesto*, handed out in April 1918 in Berlin but signed by virtually all of the Zurich and Berlin Dadaists. More importantly its first reading and subsequent publication in the German edition of *Dada* 4-5 postdates Tzara's *Manifesto Dada 1918* by almost a year. Tzara's manifesto was the bombshell that electrified what was later to become the Dada group in Paris; it was also instrumental in bringing Tzara the fame which resulted in his being invited to Paris to a hero's welcome. But its textual similarities with Serner's manifesto, and the publication in Hanover in 1920 of the considerably lengthier *Last Loosening Manifesto Dada*,[13] dated March 1918 (thus

pre-dating Tzara's manifesto, published in *Dada* 3 in December of that year), have prompted much debate as to whether Tzara was guilty of plagiarising this text. The most spectacular accusation was André Breton's denunciation of Tzara in *Après Dada* (1922), later published in his collection *Les Pas perdus*. Serner himself never made any claims one way or the other; he had known Tzara well before he allied himself with Dada, collaborated with him and Arp right till the end of Zurich Dada, and during the late phase of Zurich Dada he attended to the movement's administration as Tzara's right-hand man. In addition, Tzara would seem to have helped Serner gain a foothold in Paris by translating a text of his for the Paris magazine *Littérature*, reading from his works at Paris Dada events and by publishing him in the later issues of the magazine *Dada*. This was particularly important to Serner because his own attempts in 1920 to establish Dada in Geneva were a financial fiasco, and he became totally isolated in Switzerland once the other Dadas had moved on.

Even so, after his arrival in Paris, Serner steadily distanced himself from Tzara and indeed Dada as a whole. It would seem that this was less because of Tzara's 'plagiarism' than because Tzara was posing more and more as the originator and supremo of Dada – the first claim being untrue and the second meaningless in a movement in which, according to Tzara himself, all its members were presidents. Tzara failed to come up with a ready answer to Breton's charges, although Schrott[14] suspects that a passage from his *Dada manifesto on feeble love and bitter love*, written earlier in December 1920, may well have been directed at Serner and the question of intellectual authorship: "There are some people who have antedated their manifestos to make others believe that their own greatness manifested itself slightly earlier." In Serner's favour we have the textual similarities in the two manifestos, the fact that Serner's manifesto was already in the making as early as 1915, his famed café repartee, the fact that the *Last Loosening Manifesto* was only published in the German edition of Tzara's *Dada* 4-5, and thus omitted from the French edition read by the

people Tzara wished to impress, and the assurances of Christian Schad and Huelsenbeck of Tzara's guilt.

Yet regardless of this dispute, the *Last Loosening Manifesto* is a brilliant nihilistic *tour de force*, which, like the writings of Ball and Huelsenbeck included here, shows a continued interest in aspects of early Expressionism: in this case the cynical, paradoxical, self-referential archness of the early Expressionist poses adopted by the Berlin 'Neo-Pathetics' group, for instance, with whom Serner was in close contact in Zurich. But in Serner this self-referentiality takes on a new dimension which far surpasses that of the Expressionists or Tzara's resigned acceptance in his *Manifesto Dada 1918* of the impossibility of writing. In the *Last Loosening Manifesto*, Serner, who beside Einstein had once been the foremost art critic of *Die Aktion*, bids farewell to the possibility of any aesthetic standpoint whatsoever by advancing provocative opinions and then showing how they can just as easily be knocked over, and employing the whole gamut of poetical rhetoric while systematically undermining it with irony. Simultaneously celebrating the subjective and rendering it impossible, Serner's manifesto goes far beyond Tzara's, and several steps beyond the onslaught of the *Fantastic Prayers*: not only is the reader or listener attacked, but the author as well. As fellow Zurich Dadaist Hans Richter wrote,[15] Serner's "*Last Loosening* was in fact the final word on and definitive watchword of all that Dada meant philosophically:

everything must be loosened; not a screw must remain in its conventional place; the holes in which they once fitted must be torn out; screws and humanity on their way to new functions which can only be recognised once all that was has been negated."

While the publication of Huelsenbeck's *Fantastic Prayers* and Serner's *Last Loosening Manifesto* document the beginnings and end of Zurich Dada, Hugo Ball's *Tenderenda* has a more complicated chronology. First published in a limited edition of 1000 copies in 1967, this novel, described by Hans Arp as "Dada's secret bequest," was written between the years 1914 and 1920, and charts not only pre- or proto-Dada, but also Ball's ultimate (re)reconversion to Catholicism.

Ball started work on *Tenderenda* during his eight month stay in Berlin from 1914 to 1915, and worked on it sporadically over the years. An accurate dating of the chapters seems impossible: it is clear from his diary that he wrote three chapters in Berlin, another two in the summer of 1915, one at least in the summer of 1916, three more in early 1917, resumed work in August 1917 and wrote *The Putrefaction Conductor* in May 1919 after attending and enjoying a Dada Evening in Berlin. But Ball's dating in his diary sometimes appears erroneous, the order of the chapters may not always reflect the order in which they were written, and his diaries indicate extensive revisions. The book's three sections are generally seen as covering his pre-Dada years, Dada until Ball's first break with it in the summer of 1916, and the years up to his Catholic conversion respectively, a view which does not always seem tenable. In addition, caution must be exercised when attempting to locate individual episodes or characters in the sense of a *roman à clef*,

Hugo Ball
Tenderenda
der Phantast
Roman Arche

particularly because individual chapters seem to refer simultaneously to several episodes in Ball's life, and the protagonists often appear to be amalgams of various persons. And above all the novel is 'fantastic' – imagination and paradox reign, and although important aspects of Ball's life and thinking can be teased out, his search for primal images or 'sigils' which stir the unconscious dominates these pages.

With this in mind, certain aspects of the book deserve to be looked at in more depth, particularly in the light of Ball's ideas on language, poetry and imagination. Individual episodes and motifs are covered, where possible, in the notes at the end of this collection.

A recurring complex of themes in *Tenderenda* is the logical, the rational, the mechanical, and the war. Ball believed that under the influence of Kant and German idealism, as well as Lutheran sobriety, language had been made abstract and thus debased into a utilitarianism that allowed it to be plundered by jingoism, literary professionalism, journalism and intellectual vacuity. It had become a tool for upholding the ruling value systems and the rational and intellectualising orientation that

had produced western philosophy, art, music and religion, and was a tool for the thinking which ultimately made the war a necessity for "controlling the birth figures" (diary entry written before WW1).

During his experiments with the early Dadaists, Ball attempted to "dissolve language to the core of the creative process" in order to purify the word, find its inner essence, and immunise it from the ravages that had been done to it. Going beyond Bruitist and other experiments which were aimed at capturing the paradoxical totality of life by releasing words from their function and syntax, Ball tried to lend isolated words an invocatory,

hypnotic power and, "curiously," Ball wrote in his diary (18/6/1916), "the magically charged words conjured up and gave birth to a *new* sentence that was neither determined by, nor tied to, any conventional meaning." The process released the 'sigils' mentioned earlier, the primal forms he had already hoped to release in his theatrical schemes before the war. But it released even more. While reciting his sound poems at the Cabaret Voltaire, dressed in a cardboard 'shaman's' suit, Ball slipped into the "ancient cadences of priestly lamentation. . . For a moment I had the impression that the pale face of a disturbed youth appeared behind my Cubist mask, the half startled, half inquisitive face of a ten year-old boy who hangs, trembling and greedily, on the lips of the priests during requiems and communion at the local church. . . And, covered in sweat, I was carried from the stage, like a magic bishop." (*Diary*, 23/6/1916). Ball viewed his 'magic bishop' experience as the first re-awakening of the Catholicism of his childhood, and it is generally seen as a major reason for his inner and outward break with Dada a few days later. The magic bishop is one of the leitmotifs of *Tenderenda*.

Although Ball was to move closer and closer to the church while writing *Tenderenda*, he remained true to his 'word alchemy' or 'magic,' which was strongly tied to an aesthetic programme based not only on irrationality, primitivism and complexity, but also upon radical scepticism. This was

essential in view of the collapse of meaning and belief in things and ideas that had influenced so many artists during the first decade of the century, and which was accelerated by advances in philosophy (e.g. Nietzsche and Vaihinger), as well as in the natural sciences and psychology (from Albert Einstein to Freud) that toppled man from the pinnacle of creation. "At a closer look," wrote Ball (*Diary*, 13/11/1915), "things dissolve into phantasmata. The whole arrangement appears to be a disastrous procession of optical illusions." He felt that reality had become

fantastic, that things were "returning to chaos" and that the sceptical artist should enter the flow of the times and participate in the prevailing destruction in order to build anew. And with this breakdown, the artist who is sceptical towards handed-down meanings can use his "free, unfettered imagination. Freed to itself, the imaginative process is bound to bring those things back to light which have crossed the threshold of consciousness intact." The result will "introduce a secret language and leave behind documents full of paradox, not edification." (*Diary*, 25/11/1915). But the process of demolition and creation contains dangers: "With this demolition the elemental, the demonic will first leap out," Ball wrote, and "every word is a wish or an enchantment." *Tenderenda* is very demonic, and Ball felt the need to control the demons which populated it.

The basic tone of the novel is set by the opening chapter with the entry of a prophet. With his Expressionist phrases ("The heavens stand lemon yellow") and Zarathustrian tones (Nietzsche was a vital influence on the Expressionists, and Ball wrote a dissertation on him), his links with Ha Hu Baley (see note 40), and his similarities to the "roast poet" who appears later in the novel, and who is also clearly linked with Leybold, the prophet's appearance marks the entry of the fantastic, as exemplified by the proto-Dadaists Ball, Huelsenbeck and Leybold before the war. In addition, he proclaims a theory of relativism which he can demonstrate practically, such as by stretching his finger to the sun. This relativism is only possible once man has been removed from his pinnacle, as mentioned above, and the world is void of belief, for "belief is the measure of all things" (*Diary*, 8/4/1916).

The prophet's message falls, however, on deaf ears, and in the course of the novel Ball returns time and again to the failure of the writer and the poet. In the next chapter, for instance, a group of poets dedicated to the supremacy of subjective fantasy over intelligence and logic – clearly in the spirit of Carl Einstein (see note 42), but described ironically as a "sterilised club of fantasts" – is snubbed by the forces of law and order who have no time for their symbolism. Following this, Swaggerprance, the paragon of Decadence who features in the next chapter, and whose aesthetic programme – searching for a reality based on sensations, in both senses of the word – even extends to considering a gratuitous murder (as in Gide's *The Caves of the Vatican*, published a few years earlier), falls foul of his own

programme while attempting to fathom the reality of things. "Unable to free himself from his impressions or tame them," (*Diary*, 26/3/1916), "he succumbs to the subterranean powers" – the demons. After a brief interlude, *The Red Heavens*, in which a bruitist concert is performed by a group of animals – a different attempt to introduce reality into poetry – the next chapter, *Satanopolis*, centres on a journalist who is pursued by philistines and literati alike. His fate is equally tragic, and indeed Ball's pessimism extends throughout the novel to the very end. The writer, in whatever form, is doomed to meet with misunderstanding, death, inner uncertainty, or to be served up for general consumption as a "roast poet." The outside world appears to be too powerful, and not even Dada provides the answer. But before looking at the chapter *Grand Hotel Metaphysics*, which introduces Dada and opens the novel's second section, it is worth considering *Satanopolis* in more detail.

Captured after a pursuit, the central character, a journalist named Lilienstein, is brought to trial. His defence is nothing more than a confused mixture of Bible quotations, clichés, jingoistic phrases and advertising slogans. He is trapped in degraded language, or is unable to make himself clear in any other terms, but as Wilfried Ihrig[16] points out, he is surrounded by "magic dragons and sea-horses whizzing around above his head." Lilienstein reflects Ball's escape from the language of journalism by entering the world of the soundpoems which Ball wrote under such similar titles as 'Sea-horses and flying fish.' This notion that the journalist reflects Ball's own development is given additional strength by the fact that both the journalist and journalism are treated equivocally, and not with the vehemence Ball generally reserved for the press in his diaries.

Yet this chapter is also open to other interpretations, and all of them may have been present in Ball's mind at the time of writing: the reference to the Expressionist periodical *Die Aktion* during Lilienstein's trial ("This gentleman has no connection with the action") and to the writer Ludwig Rubiner – a principled Socialist and flag-bearer of the literati with whom Ball crossed swords on several occasions – may both suggest that the journalist is being hounded by those upholders of a moralising Socialism who published *Die Aktion*, and who objected to Ball's criticisms of their politics, as mentioned above.[17] Although this second level is evident in the chapter, it does not explain all, and a third reading could also be made on the basis of Ball's diary, which makes it clear that the chapter must have been written shortly after Ball's break with Dada in the summer of 1916, after his 'magic bishop' episode. Not only does Lilienstein escape his pursuers by going to Italy, a country Ball visited for the first time after his break, but a number of other major as well as incidental images[18] are based directly on Ball's preoccupations in his diary during the months before his brief return to Dada. Is Ball describing his flight from Dada? In *Satanopolis* a "manifesto was read out in the Devil's beer-gardens," and in his diary of this period Ball reflects on his *First Dadaist Manifesto* which he read at his last public appearance with the Dadaists, saying that it was a "scarcely veiled rejection" of his friends, and that "they felt it as such." Furthermore the journalist is identified, as mentioned previously, with "magic dragons and sea-horses": the animals of Ball's soundpoems that he had read for the first time on the evening of his 'magic bishop' experience – and by way of retribution for his misdeeds, the journalist's "paper suit" is ripped from his body, which in this context could be the famous cardboard costume Ball wore for the occasion. All of this suggests that Lilienstein is, among other things, Ball the Magic Bishop. The possibility that the journalist's flight is also from Dada as the result of his initial religious awakening, which Ball reflects on for the first time in his diary during this period, gains plausibility from the fact that the character Tenderenda – who later becomes Ball's 'religious' alter-ego – appears in the novel for the first time in the form of the chapter's narrator. In addition the lengthy parody of Christ's Passion in the form of the journalist's trial seems to underline, if ironically, Ball's new religious feelings.

No single reading can claim to be exhaustive, others suggest themselves (see note 55 on Rubiner), and it should be remembered again that the characters and events of *Tenderenda* operate on an autonomous, paradoxical level.

However, this last level of interpretation of the most complex chapter in *Tenderenda* places the next one, *Grand Hotel Metaphysics*, which Ball introduces as the "birth of Dadaism" (the only occasion he mentions Dada by name), in a different light. The birth, preceded by that of a small Jewish boy (possibly Tzara) who performs gymnastics, then by an abundance of "dishwater, scree, rubble," is finally that of one Mr Foetus "as described in Folio 28, *Ars magna*. Confucius had praised him. . . His father is Plimplam-plasko." The list is not particularly complimentary: a description from a magic book that sounds like an entry on a file card, the praise for the sage of bureaucracy and state-building, and a father whose name is taken from the title figure of an 18th century satire on the cult of genius. For all the valour the Dadaists show in this chapter in fighting off the protests and attacks delivered by the local population, who fear that the birth threatens "their barren land with fertility," the impression grows that Ball is dissatisfied with Dada. Not least politically, for the irony in the chapter's title is explained in a diary entry written the day he read this chapter at the *Galerie Dada*: "We allowed the May Day procession to march past below our Hotel Metaphysics." In this chapter Ball, the only member of Zurich Dada to be involved politically, appears to bemoan Dada's political impotence and its 'birth' as a systematised movement under the auspices of Tzara. As Ball wrote to Tzara on 15/9/1916: "I hereby declare that Expressionism, Dadaism and other Isms are the worst kind of bourgeoisie."

Thus the novel's second section, traditionally viewed as the Dada years, seems to be dealing with post-Dada*Ism*. The next chapter, *Bulbo's Prayer and the Roast Poet*, is prefaced with the words "The laughter increases to the same degree that the horror increases," but although this appears to indicate Dada's ascent in the face of the war, the chapter itself is concerned with anything but Dada humour. Bulbo's prayer is the first of four chapters of a devotional nature (the other three are each described as "Hymnus"), and from now on the book is far more concerned with Ball than Dada, as well as with a curious figure often called God, the object of these devotions. Bulbo prays for salvation not only from the war, but also from "enchantment," one of several similar words used in *Tenderenda* to describe the numbing, suggestive power of logic, utilitarianism and language unchastened by fantasy. Much of this prayer refers to the damage that is being done to the church and religion, but such lines as "they roll their drunks into your promised land at the point where hell borders paradise, and the Wagnerian yodel rings out" give a first clue to the nature of God: the debasement of his realm seems to refer in fact to the debasement of language. Hell and paradise have been reduced to the same level because language has been levelled out to produce mere words. But God cannot simply be identified as the lord of language, he proves to be too ambivalent. In this chapter he appears as a *homo logicus* wielding a table of categories, but who then accepts Bulbo's petition on account of its aesthetics, only to present the surrounding spectators with a roast poet to consume. This ambivalence becomes even stronger in the two hymns that conclude the book's second section. Not only is he praised as the "lord of the birds, dogs and cats" – the inspirer as it were of Ball's soundpoems – but also as the God of "rebellion," of "maledictions and sewers," and even as the "demon prince" and "Antichrist." More importantly the prologues to these two hymns note a "turn towards the church . . . in the vocabulary and vowels" and that "the liturgical formulae get the upper hand," once again referring to Ball the Magic Bishop. Ball's unnamed characters seem to be praying less to a deity than to the sum of what is freed in Ball by his linguistic experiments, not least the book he is writing, a wondrous slapstick mixture of the Satanic and the sublime, an amoral demon unleashed by fantasy. As Ball notes in his diary, 8/4/1916: "With its fantasy, the art of our times . . . is concerned primarily with demons, not God; it is itself demonic." These two hymns are wonderful examples of this art!

Yet the writer sees the need to control these demons, for he calls upon

Solomon who, legend tells, had a magic ring that bestowed upon him the power to control them. Later, in the closing chapters, Tenderenda also solicits the aid of St. Ambrose, a hymnologist who fought the belief in demons during the early days of the Christian church: the impression grows accordingly that the author wishes to release his word magic from the demonic. First though comes a chapter entitled the *The Putrefaction Conductor* which opens the book's third section.

This chapter, which marks the end of the war – a major theme in the first two sections – briefly returns the novel back to narrative form and Ball's less personal preoccupations. In the figure of the "Putrefaction Conductor," which is borrowed from a short play by Gottfried Benn (see note 77), Ball attacks the logical rationalism which abstracts thoughts from things and consequently enslaves the latter, now reduced to "putrefaction," to reason and control. In the second half of the chapter Ball finds time to deliver a broadside to literary professionalism in the form of a group of poets busy "recording the putrefaction and watering down the fantastic reality" with the help of machines – clearly the late Expressionists who, by the end of the war, had completely betrayed the movement's initial imaginative, anarchic, aesthetic impulse to create a maudlin form of socialism based on humanity and brotherhood. "They seem to be full of activity," says the

Putrefaction Conductor, allowing Ball another dig at *Die Aktion*. Their reply is to approach him with the words "Humanity in word and writing!" a paraphrase of the mawkish 'Oh Man!' calls of the late Expressionists, and by the end of the chapter all they want to do is devour their "cerebral cortices." The early Expressionists were often referred to favourably as 'Cerebral poets':[19] these late Expressionists merely devour this organ. But in fact they want more: they hold out their hands for money in return for their humanitarian calls. The poetry club's failure to fulfil the promise of the early Expressionists, the way it succumbed to mechanical registration and to selling poetry as a commodity, is contrasted powerfully in the next chapter by the first of two sound-poems from Ball's Dada days, *Jolifanto Bambla ô Falli Bambla*, which in the prologue is expressly linked with his magic bishop reading.

> ## KARAWANE
> jolifanto bambla ô falli bambla
> *grossiga m'pfa habla horem*
> **égiga goramen**
> higo bloiko russula huju
> **hollaka hollala**
> *anlogo bung*
> **blago bung**
> blago bung
> **bosso fataka**
> **ü üü ü**
> schampa wulla wussa ólobo
> *hej tatta gôrem*
> eschige zunbada
> **wulubu ssubudu uluw ssubudu**
> **tumba ba- umf**
> *kusagauma*
> **ba - umf**

The following chapter, the last of the three hymns, goes even further. Dedicated to "the head of his order," this hymn is not only more beatific than the previous two, but also ends with the speaker, now identified as Tenderenda, turning his back on writing and humbly following his "discreet" master, the "forefather of the hymnologists" who "lettest the animals appear within us" – pointing to Ball's growing desire to return to the "language of animals and fish, the hieroglyphic language of God."[20] This forefather seems to be St. Ambrose, who was responsible for the widespread adoption of hymns in the early church, and in the prologue to the next chapter the saint is mentioned once more: it is necessary to abjure the phantasmata of which St. Ambrose complained in order to enter monkhood. Once again, the author is suggesting that peace and quiet can only be attained by giving up demonic art. The question remains whether Ball felt this personally, and a partial answer is given by the way Tenderenda becomes closely intertwined in this chapter with Ball himself: the prologue describes Tenderenda as a "Knight of Glossy Paper" and as a fantast who set out on quixotic forays during his life – evidently the Ball of the Dada cabarets. But he is also described as a "church poet."

The first name, Laurentius, is revealing here, for it refers to St. Lawrence, also mentioned elsewhere (see note 83), and who legend tells us was roasted on a grid. So, Laurentius Tenderenda is Ball and more than Ball, a magical amalgam of Dadaist, church poet and *roast poet*, the last in the line of poets in this novel for whom poetry spells their own destruction or their ultimate inability to resist the outside world. But presumably it is the Dadaist in Tenderenda that makes him unable to accept the consequences of his calling, reclusion, for, after reviewing his whole life – quite clearly Ball's Dada days and subsequent situation – he states that he does "not know whether [he] belongs to those above or those down below." Rather like Huelsenbeck's wish in the *Fantastic Prayers* for a "cherry-brandy flip," Tenderenda simply hopes that religion will provide him with the consolation of a "Cordial Medoc." A further consolation remains though in his word-magic, for shortly before the end of the chapter he notes "a good thing though that my Pentecostal mood remains." The soundpoem that follows, described as a magic incantation, strengthens this mood. It is a statement of belief in word-mysticism, in a noumenal form of language.

This word-mysticism seems, however, to be extremely evanescent. In the concluding chapter, Tenderenda appears briefly in magic bishop guise, only to disappear into the beyond. And what initially appears to be a paradisiacal scene, where the primal, Adamic language wanders freely on a meadow in the form of an alphabet tree, proves to be an illusion. The two protagonists of this chapter, Mr and Mrs Goldhead, who can be identified as Mr and Mrs Ball, have a mystic experience and slowly realise that the world around them is really just "triangular shards of glass in outer space," and that they are victims of a spell that has been cast on them by their own son, Koko the god of the fantasts, out of revenge for being placed in the captivity of logic. The Goldheads' awakening from their 'enchantment' is short-lived, however. While Mr Goldhead prophesies the end of the spell in the form of a supernatural event: "when Metatron," a gnostic angel, "strides . . . across the firmament," the last lines of the book are thoroughly pessimistic. Mrs Goldhead mistakes the sun for a "septic ulcer," and an ironic paraphrase of a poem from Goethe's *Faust* part 2 ends with the word "depravity." Neither the Goldheads nor any of the characters previously featured in the novel manage to overcome the enchantment, the world of disbelief, putrefaction, jargon – in short a world devoid of fantasy.

In his novel, Ball takes everything to task; he criticises and writes ironically of all human effort and points to its underlying futility. Nor does Ball give any prescriptions or answers, and in almost Serneresque fashion he assiduously charts the failure of the one thing he champions: imagination. Yet the novel is composed of exactly this, a brilliant example of what is released when the alienated stuff of the world is subjected to unfettered imagination. But in a line in the prologue to 'Laurentius Tenderenda,' the character is compared with an exorcist, and as he completed the novel, Ball compared the work with "that well-sealed magical shrine in which the Jews of old believed they held Asmodeus captive." (*Diary*, 15/7/-1920). The novel releases the demonic and Ball tries in vain to fight this with his word magic. Ball was relieved when he finally finished *Tenderenda*, his last literary work, and hoped that his demonic "attacks of wickedness" might finally be

quelled.

Yet even if Ball was to return to Catholicism shortly after the book's completion, it seems over-literal to believe that this was a return to the religion of his childhood, as his contemporaries described it. Even after he had completed *Tenderenda*, Ball did not discard his aesthetic programme but simply shifted its emphasis, as is hinted at by the novel's finishing touch, the quotation from Bernard de Clairvaux on the first page. Ball had found it in an anthology of mystic poetry edited by Remy de Gourmont entitled *Le Latin mystique*,[21] a book he read the same week that he finished *Tenderenda*. The anthology was a revelation to Ball; he saw in it the "unification of all [his] longings and strivings" over the years, stating that

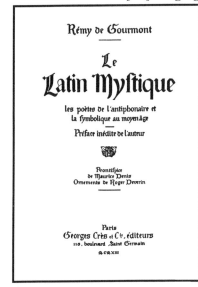

for these poets, whom he describes as ascetics, monks and priests who lived solely for the beyond, "verse is the ultimate expression of the essential nature of things, and thus, hymn and prayer. Their poetry is one of the mysterious sigil, of divine names, of the spiritual extract." It would seem from this that Ball had found at last a 'purer' form of word-mysticism, a poetry concerned primarily with God, not demons. But the anthology is telling: it is a compendium of religious decadence, in which the licentious, morbid and sinful —

50

the demonic in Ball's sense – is given far more poetic presence than the chaste and 'religious.' Ball's re-conversion to Catholicism was that of the dandy and decadent, rather 1890's in fact – a significant aspect of the Dadaist who had written *Tenderenda*; since Dada, as Ball reflected in his diary in May 1917, was "a masque, a peal of laughter. And behind it was a synthesis of the romantic, dandyish and – demonic theories of the 19th century."

— Malcolm Green

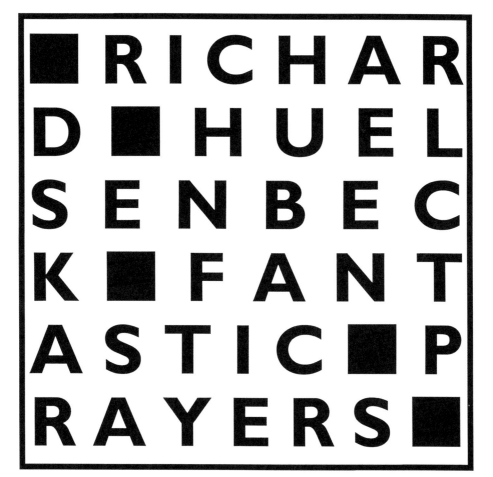

RICHARD HUELSENBECK FANTASTIC PRAYERS

```
■ P L
A N
E ■
```
pig's bladder kettle drum cinnabar cru cru cru

theosophia pneumatica

the great spiritual art = *poème bruitiste* performed

for the first time by Richard Huelsenbeck DaDa

or or birribum birribum the ox whizzes round in a circle or contracts for

casting light hand grenade parts 7.6 cm chauceur

admixture Soda calc. 98/100%

setter damo birridamo holla di funga qualla di mango damai da dai umbala

damo

brrs pffi commencer Abrr Kpppi commence start start

sbeen taken fer 'ome since terday

work

work

breh breh breh breh breh breh breh breh breh

sokobauno sokobauno sokobauno

Schikaneder Schikaneder Schikaneder[22]

the dustbins are growing fat sokobauno sokobauno

the dead rise up from within wreaths of flaming torches about their heads

behold the way the horses are bent over the water butts

behold the rivers of paraffin are falling from the crests of the moon

behold the way Lake Orizunde reads the newspaper and eats its beef steak

behold the bone cancer sokobauno sokobauno

behold the placenta as it screams in the butterfly nets of the high-school

boys

sokobauno sokobauno

the priest closeth his trou-ouserfly rataplan[23] rataplan his trou-ouserfly and

55

his hair juts ou-out of his ears

the buckcatapult fa-alls from the sky the buckcatapult and the grandmother hoiks up her breasts

we puff the flour from our tongues and shout and the head wanders about
on the gable

the priest closeth his trou-ouserfly rataplan rataplan his trou-ouserfly and
his hair juts ou-out of his ears

the buckcatapult fa-alls from the sky the buckcatapult and the grandmother hoiks up her breasts

we puff the flour from our tongues and shout and the head wanders about
on the gable

wireheadgametot ibn ben zakalupp wau woi zakalupp tailbone oxy-hydro-
blow-piping

sweat-stained O shaveling-giblets heaven'severin

has a growth in his joint

belu blue always blue bloompoet yellows the antlers

beer bar obibor

baumabor botschon ortischell seviglia

O ca sa ca ca sa ca ca sa ca ca sa ca ca sa ca ca sa

hemlock in skin purpuration swells on little wormy and monkey has hand
and backside

O ta chipulala O ta Mpota masses

Mengulala mengulala kulillibulala

Bambosha bambosh

the priest closeth his trou-ouserfly rataplan rataplan his trou-ouserfly and
his hair juts ou-out of his ears

chupuravanta burroo pupaganda burroo

ischarimunga burroo his trou-ouserfly his trou-ouserfly

kampampa kamo his trou-ouserfly his trou-ouserfly

katapena kamo katapena kara

Chuvuparanta da umba da umba da do[24]

da umba da umba da umba he he

his trou-ouserfly his trou-ouserfly

Mpala the glass the eye-tooth trara

katapena kara the poet the poet katapena tafoo

Mfunga Mpala Mfunga Koel

dytiramba toro and the ox and the ox and the toe covered in verdigris by
the stove

Mpala tano mpala tano mpala tano mpala tano ojoho mpala tano mpala
tano ja tano ja tano ja tano O his trou-ouserfly[25]

Mpala Zufanga Mfisha Daboscha Karamba juboscha dabo eloe

Slowly the huddle of houses opens the centre of its body

■	T
R	E
E	■

then the swollen throats of the churches screamed into the depths above them

here they hunted like hounds the colours of every earth that had ever been seen every sound that had ever been heard plummeted rattling to the central point.

the colours and sounds smashed like glass and cement and soft dark drops fell heavily.

now the stars snarl in time and stretch up the palms of their hands.

O Allah Cadabaudahojoho O hojohojolodomodoho

O Burrubu hihi O Burrubu hihi O hojolodomodoho

and white starched codgers ho

and puffed up poodles ho

and madly arched kiosks ho

and those hours that are filled with the bass trumpets' shine

seriously drunk bassoons wander on the railing spikes and barrels red-liveried swollen junks ho

Oho oho O mezza notte which bore the tree

the shadow-whips now lash round your body

white is the blood that you feed on across the horizons

the gaily decked ships sail between the intervals of your breath

Oho oho the cry of the centuries whizzes across the mirror of your body

the preened thunderstorms sit in your hair like parrots

there are paper streamers and gold tinsel in the furrows of your brow

every form of perishing lies buried before you oho

behold millions of grave-crosses are your midday meal

the cadence of your dress is like ebb and flow
and when you sing the rivers dance before you
Oho joho so you sing and thus your voice works
O Alla Cadabaudahojoho O hojohojolodomodoho
O Burrubu hibi O Burrubu hihi O hojohojolodomodoho

The rivers flow from the speckled tubes into the shade of R I
the living trees V E
parakeets and vultures keep falling from the twigs to the ground R S

the walls of the sky are raffia mats and the great parachutes of the magicians descend from the clouds
the towers have clapped masks of cloudskin over their dazzling eyes
O you rivers Under the ponte dei sospiri entangle yourselves on lungs and livers and severed throats
but in Hudson Bay flew the siren or a griffin bird or a human female of the latest kind
you stick your hands in the pockets of the parliamentary secretaries which are full of pensions all manner of goodwill and lovely liver sausages
what haven't we done before you my how we all prayed
the holy singers' backsides swell from the scorpion's sting and Ben Abka the high priest rolls in muck
your veins are blue red green and orange coloured like the faces of the ancestors who squat on the edge of the altars in Sunday suits
top hats giant ones O made of pewter and bronze perform a heavenly concert
the figures of the angels float around your exit as the reflection of poisonous blossoms
so arrange your members over the horizon in the cascades
the Indian Ocean climbed up from its divan its ears stuffed with cotton wool
the hot waters creep from their huts and scream
they have erected tents over your ardour from morning till night and

hordes of phonographs wait for the whimpering of your lust

a calamity has befallen the world

the breasts of the giant lady went up in flames and an Indian rubber man
gave birth to a rat's tail

Umba Umba the negroes tumble out of the chicken hutches and the froth
of your breath skims their toes

a great battle passed over you and over the sleep of your lips

a great carnage filled you up full

DADADADA

THE DAME who had attained her former stature
the impotence of the street sweepers has become scandalous
who can say I am since he am and you art dulce et decorum
est pro patria mori or be loyal and faithful or then someone fell flat or one
biff and you're left in your shirtsleeves who dares be knight or page and
there's a surging and seething and bubbling and hissing Concordia shall be
thy name the giraffes are already boring their heads into the sand and still
the calfskin thunders right what do you want from me with my tender
years one beauty chases the other and the polar hare leaped from the tailbone O ah O the negresses race along the slopes of the mountains beating
their drums furiously some crawl others fly some burst others trudge along
and so many downwards lengthwise what do people want from me with
my tender years the young monkeys skid down my hair as quick as a flash
the blue horses graze on the surfaces of my teeth the RHINOCEROS squats
alternately in my breasts buzz buzz hop hop hop buzz buzz hop hop hop
who brought the panther into the tram who kicked the old aunt in her
rubber bum it was I ladies and gentlemen I am the great event since
sunrise three children presented me with Mafarka the Futurist[26] and
already the third is simmering in the casserole of sparkling steel for how
did father Homer put it bash her thrash her thump her until the absinthe
dances in her capillary tubes I am the pope and the promise and the latrine
in Liverpool.

THE PHILOSOPHER (IMPROVISATION)

The ironweed burns in the deep wells on the day of the moon far out over the Indian Ocean hangs the moon of its body spindle locust hail and storm and the run-up of the red ghosts the cockerels' cooing the salamanders' minuet — O the sky's living brimstone burns before you

smokes before you you bear an amethyst under your tongue

your eye's fiery ray stretches to the Pillars of Hercules you walk like honey

across the rivers and the land lies before you like the belly of a woman

the bloody sand falls from the throats of the swallows

part of this earth is red but others are white

high priests and parsons surge up like mist into cypresses behind the agave stems

O you fluttering stone — behold — behold

behold O the envyweed where the people's faces turn dark

like the coat of a roebuck is your soul on which the bugs dance

in the first quarter of the double moon your mother gave birth to the boy moor

sasa sasa chimes fall from the mountains and kettle drums roll into the river that is there called Athos

fig-warts fall from your body and the damage done by cancer is like sage

O you fish glue of our virtues O you hare-sweat of our fortune

the frogs already explode in the egg yolks of the large birds

the wall of the tall dome is already cast in shadow

the flame fell from the stars like a burning house

the papier maché elephants crept from the signs of the zodiac

sasa sasa then the lemon tree shot up from the artesian wells

and cinnamon fell on our town and garlic like a storm

the ravens' circles lemon yellow
darkest cold shadow walls
of the shadow walls has the masks'
O O ho oho in wood-carved legs
association and Baudelaire Mafarka blossoms
the cherry tree blossoms blue bell chime
slowly it rises from the darkness falls from the whiteness towards him flies faster and smashes the perspectives resolves itself hastily in the giant surfaces teaches adoration calls the yellow the red O the Red Indian red the totem calls the death knell calls the umbrellas madder red glide float over the fountains and sitting and seated and seated and laughing and seated and laughing is the kai-aiserin of porcelain the kai-aiserin the dragons cast their tongues from the capitals O — O — O — the capitals are ablaze the blue flames of the capitals flash across the seas the seas are brightly coloured under the sound of the flames O — O the lassos fly out as far as the equator

■ CHO
RUS ■
SANC
TUS ■

a a o	**a e i**	**i i i**	**o i i**
u u o	u u e	u i e	a a i
ha dzk	drrr en	obn br	buss boom
ha haha	hihihi	lilili	leiomen

"indigo indigo
"tramway sleeping bag
"bug and flea
"indigo indigai
"umbaliska
"boom DADAI

■THE■IN
DIAN■OC
EAN■AND
■THE■UT
TERLY■R
ED■SUN■

Everything climbed up higher everything sank into the heights

large pupils swivel with a rattle on the galleries of cedar wood

the Christmas trees wander in my breath like specks of dust

hurdy-gurdy sound falls from the mouth of the elephants in the night

someone shouted but at the eleventh hour; raise your skirts shake out your trousers and take the kettle drum out of your knee joint let the coffee cups fall from the height of your chests

OJOHO OJOHO the hordes of young sea-cows crept out of the sewers

everything broke round the moon but here sat the stuffed birds on long brass perches

everything fluttered apart and the thunderbolt rose from the purple foliage

O hear my prayer you toady-spinsters and rat-catchers

O hear my prayer you masseurs and sea urchins which you ride on the peaks of the fountains in the magnificence of your robes

the mandarins are here and have hung up their fat to dry

O haibjukutuolamaturrubsk zerripstipipp zerripstipipp

tallubolala tallubolala zerripstipippstipipp

for the pastors and forestry apprentices fall from the Tour Eiffel in their cherry pink uniforms

sulphurous vapours rise from the cadavers which float down the rivers

everything bulged upward everything lost its sand and danced in the aeroplane

the black pieces break out of the neck the profusion stretches out

the blackness stretches out and sings the singing stretches out
tallubolala tallubolala O hear my prayer
behold my larynx of glossy paper and beeswax
the twelve shot men dance around the cowherd who is deaf and dumb
between my shoulder blades wanders Tzara the poet
Tzara the poet wanders with a top hat and parasol
with parasol and top hat wanders Tzara the poet
he wipes the sweat from his forehead
he tears the laurel wreath from his leg
O Tzara O O embryo O head full of blood and wounds

```
■ T H E ■
K E T T
L E ■ D
R U M ■
```
HOHOHOHOHO where is the crematorium that rose from the rivers the mighty DADA descended the rope ladder the poetry schools have been washed away down the sewers the green piston thrusts out of my head farting and blustering

HOHOHOHOHO

I am the beginning of the world inasmuch as I am the end

did you ever see the car in its pyjamas it is packed to the brim with frogs and tows a blue cloud behind it on a cable it whistles round the peaks of monte maladetta and the young Spanish girls waved to it with their wisdom tooth which is as large as the isle of Madagascar and inside it is an avenue where the bees can be seen strolling in their Sunday best

I warn you extinguish the sun and let the slowworms leap out of their cases for one must not count one's chickens before they are hatched

I warn you the lacquered negroes will arrive unexpectedly and empty the butts over the tulip bed

I hear the carpenter's shop in the belly of the little fishes

who can doubt then in the ascension of the speaking man the Lord has given and the Lord shall take away again

and yet the entry price is just 50 centimes who hasn't seen the fat-devils as they grease their auburn hair they bark from their armpits as the Barbary stallion leaps into the coffee pot

a spindle hums in the casement of your body but who can doubt then in the ascension of the speaking man

Cages stuffed full of fat red apes

a lady who climbed up a house legs first

10,000 clerks small bluish shabby clerks who disappear in clouds of steam as they approach the horizon

the walls of Jericho large wind instruments a conductor's rostrum with a hunchback wearing a crown and tails

Screams which turn into people giant bronze bells which fall into the sea waterspouts yellow inestimably large waterspouts which resemble Messrs Beethoven

I see people people people who wave a billion arms above their heads

very ceremonial extraordinarily ceremonial the blackness the whole infinity of the bass trumpets' sound which glides over the broad surfaces which glides over the broken surfaces which smashes with a crash smashes wood it smashes something with a four-thousandfold bang the bellies the tautly distended beautiful all-too beautiful brown bellies burst HAHAHA the head of the donkey the large papier maché head with its mother of pearl eyes the yellowest donkey HAHA — now we are one with ourselves and now the living child falls out of the nostril now the blue ice grotto is like Bullier like Madrid in the hot sun

beh bumm beh bumm O I slatebone och

I glue-cocoon beh bumm beh bumm

weep no more Katharina weep no more O Josef because the church has been built once more of liquor

oh hover in solitude on the ladder's rungs

HOLY HOLY

HOLY HOLY

they blow the coloured snow from out of their eyes
wax dolls climb onto the xylophone
HOLY HOLY
HOLY HOLY
SANTA CLARA

The damned steal up to rivers
their eyes hanging over beards and necks
tricky shades float mortally weary from out of the barracks
still sputtering testy curses amidst the tumult
the Buddha's belly grows in the lily pond
encircled by flitting birds whose whitewashed beaks repaint the surface
vomit on Fuji while climbing the volcanos
the cavaliers' magnificent array glides along gently
the billow surges ashore and flies apart
but there is danger of fire in Yoshiwara
and it delivers fast whip-cracks around the loins

```
■ M E I
S T E R
S I N G E
R ■ D E
A T H ■
```

Great pensive ass for centuries on end
Adorned with pigs' bladders accustomed to mediaeval oboes
And flute concerts and the express train see how he travels via Vlissingen —
Ha he's travelling there (you can't see it) with the corpse in the corner
Blinking philosophically distorted grimaces behind his lids
The belly fat already slightly crinkled smelling bad — Oh God
Priest Salome bom bom take one ace of spades wins
But he who still kissed his wife before mounting his iron steed
The abomination and he had his aunt insured the good man
Yes Lord of almighty bared teeth of rotting livers
Mutilated horses sundust and guts distending
Like houses gigantic blue blue gigantic houses
Yes Lord you colossal negro in the battle on the
Throne of skulls Oh your legs are worth it
Sensible song I sing to you spring is and revolution
Small girls for you to devour small yellowish tame
Who bear their breasts like Cheviot salt he said
No no no longer soldier no one wants that any more
But he who flees shall not curse thee for thine is the kingdom
And eternity and all backsides

Streetcar hey hey your fire tongs in the night

The lord with the wine bottle pitches like a ship

Now the night must give us a thundering clout about the head

The tall top hats dance an incredible funeral service

An arc lamp smashes on your skull you old race-track swindler

Gold rattles in your sack your face cracks in two

Hey lighting currents blue and red lighting currents along the cable off and away

And the moon which laughs affably

And the tree tops which descend on the sergeants' kisses

Hey hey the street rolls along in front of us like a table coaster

Seated at the table is father with the milk bowl in his hand

It is still wartime and people keep reciting the same prayer

But meanwhile the fire is being stoked under the boilers of the machines

The stoker buckles his leather belt round his scrawny hips

Hey hey it is the hour when the safe-crackers are out and about

It is the hour when the consumptives wheeze in their sweaty beds

Just look how the doctor opens his pincette with an ironic glance

But the moon laughs affably old rhinoceros

Where the maid gave birth to a son in the hay ricks

May Christ arise he who carries the world in his head

Yes a most unimaginable scream which echoes from the sewers

Electric light racing through ice grottoes

Bells booming through fairground bellowing

Automaton-man sneaking through softly

May night May night Oh your breasts trimmed with lavender
As if trimmed with tumours announcing victory
A new victory with flags and Hindenburg and an edict
from our Kaiser

Your leg hangs over me like a sickle moon
quite clear: your breasts breathe two young animals
behind the best Brussels lace
hey garçon: café au lait — le matin please and a glass of
water

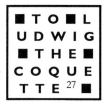

Basically you are like your sisters who with wobbling bellies creep
anxiously along the sewers listening
for the whistle of the vice squad and the carnivorous pimps
The meat trader whose trousers you stole with his wallet of alligator skin
has told me all there is to know about your soul
hey — you old pig: you are 50 now but the high-school boys still dream
fervently of you
They dream: you arrive softly with your supple cane
tanning their backsides to their heart's content
hey you old roués and white slavers you gypsies and hotel thieves
pray pray if you think it's fun
Or get really blasted on top of the houses crash onto the gutter
let the fire brigade thunder up chase the rivers from your sleep
old rabble a bottle under my arm I approach you you crazed ghosts
Is that you again gorgeous sow has the surgeon already
spotted your belly grappling irons at the ready torches and iodoform
Dada! Dada! nothing lives apart from you sweet lover

Greater than the beef steak is death

he walks through the land with those monstrous eyes like two cinnabar-clouds

so that the sun sinks in pale fear the policeman freezes
and the sea screams what a miracle in its sleep
yes processions of hearses jostling waggons with well-fed corpses
also virgins on whose lips and brows the kiss has turned stiff
mother's body convulsed the immeasurable made by god
yes he sings more powerfully than the priests' litanies
sending up steam and trumpets' call
nations burst apart little grumblers children yes hopeless pleading
God God God he flings the cloak round his loins
breathes into the cities where lying weeping and inconsolable on beds
we are forced to comprehend the incomprehensible
he descends on shoulders and necks before we realise
strokes soft cheeks and mouth hound
Almighty killer revolutionary
we are respect and simultaneously disrespect
which we humans form in your likeness

For Li (24.11.19)

You have no eyes

Your bellies are large copper drums

The hearses wheel across your ear with wailing and weeping

O — O behold the noses which hang on the door leaves

We hold our fist in our hand and sing the Watch on the Rhine[28]

We take the soup tureen and fall silent in awe

The flame leaped out from the city and the fish stand in rank and file

Behold the postman and the bosom of the prima donna

The clergymen have organised themselves

The ash cans have organised themselves

Murder is trumps

Thus be blessed among women

Old boy (it's time — it's time)

For Hans Kasiske[29]

■ H	
Y M	
N ■	

O you metal bird which flutters in the sign of Cancer

O you transparent heart and coffee pot above the blue parapets of my castle

O you metal bird and vulture O you ascension of my soul from a cnuckabout[30]

Avu Avu buruboo buruboo the madmen are free and the pope rises up

The eye falls out and the pipe broke

Littipih littipih O you two soft downed hands of my soul

O you horse of my soul you bassoon of my bride

O you sal volatile of the donkey you snakeskin

Ayo doldeldoh ayo doldeldoldeldoh

Large brass pots fall from the hearths

The soubrettes jump from the windows and scream

The cadavers of the university professors arrive clay pipes in their mouths

The corpses of the embryos grow round my forehead like groves

My forehead is pregnant with seven cows and juts out sideways

It juts out sideways — O you wretched vulture

For behold for behold I am the *demon*

Oho yodeldoh oho rataplan

My thighs are fruit barges

But my arms are fly whisks

Littipih littipih for behold — for behold

The mosquitoes climb from the railway trains canes in their hands

The lovely athletics clubs ride on the penguins

O swing your arm O swing your leg

O you metal bird of my soul — O you wretched vulture

The great stone balls hold their midday meal
Once the game is finished the fleas emigrate
Then the land is empty
Many more people must hunger
Take the sword of justice and pierce the piss-pot
Take the sun and shake your trouser leg
All that must be thought over carefully
The lions have arrived unexpectedly in my fireplace
My head fell unexpectedly on my backside
Teremmtete remmte[31]
We want to love our fatherland the grand cheese-cake
And the moon and old Bismarck
And the boats that sail round the mashed potatoes
at midnight

```
■ T H E
■ C Y L
I N D E
R ■ G A
B L E ■
```

Then the Dadasopher[32] rose from the seat of the Giant-Dada-privy and delivered the following speech   I am the Dadasopher from the beginning till the end of time   I hold the whisky bottle in my left hand and the eraser in my right   You can all go and   The alphabet letters dance up out of my ears and my belly sends out waves of excitement to the beat of the Hohenfriedberger[33]   I lash my whip from East to West and the young lice whom I wish well rejoice on my fingers   My head lies in the Nile and my legs hack open the polar sea but no one knows what good that is   That is Dadaco[34] the book of the sun but even the sun doesn't know what good that is   Behold the white steam which spreads from my nostrils over the earth — behold the shadows cast by my lips   I am the new moon who stands in rubber boots as the trains depart I am the calf that climbs onto the rain gutter during the military parade   yes yes that astonishes you earth-slouchers and slow-worms so that you rub your noses on the petrol tank but we haven't heard the end of the matter yet

Someone arrived with an accordion and struck up a dance for the elephants   I am the meteor which plummets from the nipples of the moon   I am the cylinder gable which John Heartfield constructed   Hey you excavators and knackers stretch open your bellies and tread your hair under foot   The judgement begins the great day of reckoning has arrived.

Things have really gone too far in this world

Cows sit on the telegraph poles and play chess

The cockatoo under the Spanish dancer's skirts is singing

as sadly as a regimental bugler and the cannon wail

the whole day long

Such was the lilac landscape which Mr Smith was talking about when he lost his eye

Only the fire brigade can drive the nightmare from the drawing room but all the hoses are torn

Yes yes Sonia they take the celluloid doll for a changeling and scream: God save the king.

The entire Monist Society[36] is gathered on the steamship "Meyerbeer"

but only the helmsman has any clue about top C

I pull the anatomical atlas from out of my toe

a serious study begins

Have you seen the fish that are standing in front of the opera house in cutaways

already for two nights an' two days?

Ah ah you great devils — ah ah you beekeepers and sergeant majors

Wanna woof woof woof wanna where where where who today has not heard what our Father Homer wrote

I have both war and peace in my toga but I'll take a cherry-brandy flip

No one knows today whether tomorrow he will be past history

They beat time to it with a coffin lid

If only someone had the courage to tug the tail feathers out of the tram it would be a great age

The zoology professors gather on the meadow
They hold the rainbow at bay with the palms of their hands
The great magus places tomatoes on his forehead
The roebuck whistles the stallion bounds
If you haunt the castle and its grounds
(Who wouldn't end up gaga at that?)

Slip **O slip the electric railways over your arms and** smash in the town hall remove the swans from the lily fields and the screen from the princess's bed for evidently O for evidently then everything must come about come about must everything must everything come about in the earth allez-oop I chanced Oh into my grandmother's belly eiovai eiovai my skull is red and perforated and the beautiful intestines bulge out of it when the grandfather clock strikes so slip O slip the bathtubs over your calves for the frightful faces are already whizzing round the schoolmaster's head for one can already see Aristotle's spirit on the periphery of the citadel he wears kid leather gloves O eiovaih O

wearing red aprons the women dwarfs carry the steamer away

behold the jungle hanging on the ridges of their hunches and the cries of the kangaroos

and already the chimney-sweeps fall from the meshes of the sky

the dynamo stops and the luxury train flies along silently through the necks and bodiced breasts of the tightrope dancers

the evening is laid to rest in the trouser seats of morocco leather

the Ferris wheels tumble out of the birds nests and oh there are no more cries from the donkey which had already lain on its back to give birth

```
■ S O U
L ■ S
O ■ B
L U E ■
```

Your soul old buccaneer with its sou'wester ascends over Lake Zurich in three-four time shrouds itself from the influence of the night

his Chinese lantern-soul rises in the breath of the putrid forest

echo of the revolution's glory of the freshly vacated bed

cities leaving a scandal in their wake

hardly a person pricks the sun with his parasol

neither Professor Knatschke nor President Ebert[37] nor you

but the soul deeply blanching din spreading zigzag

embracing

it floats ha over the carousels and saltimbanques scarcely recalling the 2,50 for the chamber maid

that is the onslaught of the miracles the organisation of all wax figures

a great hallali in Macao or the drunkenness in Mexico City lala

no one knows the hour of retribution blue in blue

where love is dressed up as cheques on the money changers' table with the refinement accrued down the centuries

no one thinks of the horse munching his hay and reading his bible

kindred to his head kindred to the tramway kindred to the bell which rings under water as the great steamer approaches

Just the soul ascending in three-four time over Lake Zurich

no more revelations in its presence indeed no Feast of Tabernacles

The ships' figure-heads are pulled up and down the soul and the soul's pockets detach themselves from the moon we have converted the Red Indians and the whores who were guilty of diabolic vice I have spent eight days kissing the stone on which our Lord Jesus set his foot as he rose into heaven a blond boy chastises  me each morning before the sun rises and the frogs drink my holy blood I cast my eyes behind me and the customs men and sinners danced on them until they gasped their last I cross the Rubicon the sacraments whirl in my head my mules climb up above the cities and the people pray to them O I hold the shadow-roofs and clay tablets before me as if for my personal joy who is to stop me earth rises up before me with a cry
ABBA ABBA[38] call the wise men who follow my step
when I hold my breath there comes a wailing from the graves
when I dance the wolves say to their young
cold lord cold lord just like him
O yes certainly but not completely
YOU ARE MY WAY AND THE TRUTH
YOU SHOULD BIDE BY ME.

O vous, messeigneurs et mes dames,
Qui contemplez ceste painture,
Plaise vous prier pour les âmes
De ceulx qui sont en sepulture.

Saint Bernard [39]

THE PROPHET'S ASCENT

We find ourselves amidst the flurry and excitement of an imaginary city. A new god is expected. Thunderhead (who does not appear elsewhere in the novel) has transferred his residence to a tower from which he distributes motley bulletins with the aim of reporting on developments. A balmy evening closes in. Enter a charlatan who offers the prospect of an ascension. He has even conceived his own theory on this, which he expounds at great length. It is thwarted, however, by the public's scepticism. The consequences of this.

On this day Thunderhead was prevented from attending the ceremonials. Behold, he sat before atlases and compasses and proclaimed the wisdom of the higher spheres. He unfurled long papyrus rolls, painted with animals and symbols, from his tower in order to warn the people standing beneath the nests against the screaming hordes of angels who were circling the tower in rage. But on this day someone carried through the city a sign on a long staff, bearing the legend:

Talita kumi, arise little maid;
Thou art the one, thou shalt be the one.
Daughter of the gutter,
Mother of rejoicing,
The strung up and banish'd,
The locked up and burned,
Cry out to thee.
Free us, O bless us,

Thou who art unknown,
Stand forth!

With fasting and purgatives the city prepared itself for the appearance of a new God, and already there appeared many among the crowd who claimed to have encountered Him in the throng. A warning was issued, wherein was writ that whosoever should be caught visiting or trespassing upon the bell-wheels or rag-towers without due authorisation would be slain alive. The causal nexus was pumped up afresh and left for all to see as food for the holy spiders. With rattles and bagpipes, the hand-wringing coffee- and supplication-processions of scholars and artists wended their way. But from every draught and dormer watermarks hung and the glass syringes towered. Then the prophet strode with violet face[40] across the market square as if prearranged, and, commanding the laughing houses, the stars, the moon and the crowd, said:

"The heavens stand lemon yellow. Lemon yellow stand the fields of the soul. Our heads are crooked to the ground and we have opened our ears wide. We have spread out our aprons and habits and our back of crazed china glints compliantly.

"Verily I say unto you: my humility is not for you to judge, but for   GOD alone. Each seeks a happiness for which he is inadequate. No one has many enemies, so many as he could have. Man is a chimera, a miracle, a divine approximation, full of malice and deceit.

"One day, out of curiosity and suspicion, I no longer recognised myself. And lo, I turned round and examined my soul. And lo, there burned the candle and it dripped upon my own skull. My first realization however was: small and large, that is folly; large and small, that is relativity. And lo, my finger then flew forth and burnt itself on the sun. And lo, the hand of the clock tower tore up the stones of the street. But you believe you can feel, and are felt."

He paused for a moment to box his ear, then threw a glance at the fifth storey of the fourth building, where Lunette's pink silken leg extended out of the window. Sitting on it were two winged creatures, sucking blood.

And the prophet continued:

"Verily, nothing is the way it appears. Rather it is possessed of a vital spirit and goblin which remains motionless as long as one looks at it. But once discovered, it transforms itself and becomes monstrous. For years on end I bore the burden of things wishing for liberation. Until I saw and recognised their dimensions. And I was seized by fervour. Odious life! And I stretched out my arms in defence, and flew, flew straight as an arrow over the roofs."

It was clear that the prophet, dazzled by the bluster of his own words, had been unable to avoid making vain promises. Flapping loudly with both hands he rose up and flew, as if making a test flight, a good distance into the evening, then curved back and, with a couple of hops, alighted gently.

The rabble, hanging by their waists from the windows on all sides of the marketplace, was alarmed; but, astonished by this spectacle, they shook their heads in sceptical displeasure, waved frantically the salt trumpets and paper lanterns they had brought along, and shouted:

"The magnifier! The magnifier!"

For it was well known that the prophet often employed such a glass on his excursions, and so it was thought that the whole business was merely a swindle, that the prophet had used such devices to cloak his tricks. There was also an intermezzo: an inquisitive woman who had fluttered violently from a flag pole, was torn from it and swept eastwards over the roof tops by the evening wind. Moreover, a cockerel with a rudely plucked crest flew high over the ladies' fans, which was seen as a mark of resourceful vanity.

Disheartened and dismayed, the prophet did indeed pull the magnifier from his pocket. A mirror, incidentally, which had the girth of the Ferris wheels that can be seen at fairs. The exquisitely polished glass was mounted in silver and elegantly affixed to a long wooden handle. He raised this mirror high above his head in a tragic pose, suddenly soared aloft, smashed the mirror, the shards clattered, and he vanished in the yellow seas of the evening.

But the splinters from the magic glass sliced through the houses, sliced through the people, the cattle, the tightroperies, the pit tunnels and all the unbelievers, so that the count of the gelded mounted from day to day.

```
■ J O H A N
N ■ T H E
■ C A R O
U S E L ■
H O R S E ■
```

It is the summer of 1914. A fantastical community of poets smells a rat and resolves to bring its symbolic hobby-horse, Johann, into safe keeping before it's too late. How Johann first resists and then consents. Odysseys and obstacles under the leadership of one Benjamin. An encounter in distant lands with Big Chief Fireshine,[41] who proves however to be a police informer. Following this a historiological observation on the labour pains of a police dog in Berlin.

"One thing's for certain," said Benjamin,[42] "intelligence is dilettantism. Intelligence no longer fools us. They look in, we look out. They are Jesuits of utility. As intelligent as Savonarola, no such thing. As intelligent as Manasse, no problem. Their bible is the book of civil law."

"Quite right," said Jopp, "intelligence is suspicious: the cunning of jaded advertising bosses. The society of ascetics, "The Hideous Leg," invented the Platonic idea. Nowadays the "thing in itself" is a brand of shoe polish.[43] The world is cocky and full of epilepsy."

"Enough," said Benjamin, "It makes me sick when I hear the words "law" and "contrast" and "so" and "consequently." Why must the Zebu be a humming-bird? I hate addition and baseness. When a seagull preens its wings in the sun one should leave it at that and not say "so" to it, it suffers as a result."

"So," said Borejay, "let's bring Johann the Carousel Horse into safe keeping and strike up a song to the fabulous."

"I'm not sure," said Benjamin, "it'd be better if we brought Johann the Carousel

Horse into safe keeping. There are portents that bad things are in the offing."

And there were indeed portents that bad things were in the offing. A head had been found which cried "Blood! Blood!" incessantly, and parsley grew over its cheekbones. The thermometers were full of blood and the muscle extensors functioned no longer. The "Watch on the Rhine"[44] was being discounted in the banking houses.

"Fine, fine," said Borejay, "let us bring Johann the Carousel Horse into safe keeping. You can never tell what the future might bring."

Johann the Carousel Horse stood, large-eyed and bathed in sweat, on the sky-blue threshing floor. "No, no," said Johann, "here I was born and here I shall die." But that was an untruth, for Johann's mother hailed from Denmark[45] and his father was Hungarian. They managed, however, to reach an agreement and flew that very night.

"Parbleu," said Borejay, "the world has come to an end. There's a wall here. We can't go any further." Indeed, there was a wall in front of them. It ascended vertically to the sky.

"Ridiculous," said Jopp, "we've lost our touch. We've ventured into the night without remembering to hang weights on ourselves. No wonder we're drifting in the air."

"Poppycock," said Borejay, "there's something fishy going on here, I won't go any further. Look at the fishheads lying about. Catfish have been at work here. They've been weaving a yarn of sand here."

"The Devil only knows," said Puckerman, "I also find it a bit eerie. Someone's about to pull the wool over our charlatans' eyes!" He was shaking violently.

"Stop everyone!" Benjamin commanded. "What's that over there? A paddy wagon? Black with barred windows? What's that growing over there? Agaves, fan-palms and tamarinds? Jopp, look in the book of omens and see what it all means."

"A paddy wagon among agaves," said Borejay, "that's a nasty predicament. Very dodgy. Lord knows what we've got ourselves into."

"Nonsense," called Benjamin, "if it wasn't dark we could see perfectly well what's up. That quack of a horse doctor pointed us in the wrong direction."

"The fact is," said Jopp, "we're standing in front of a wall. We can't go any further. Ivypatch, light the lantern." Ivypatch rummaged in his bag but all he produced was an enormous, light-blue organ pipe. But he took it along all the same.

"Step closer, gentlemen," came a sudden voice, "you're all up the garden path." It was Big Chief Fireshine. "What's all this nocturnal groping about? And why the get-up? Take off those celluloid noses! Unmask yourselves! Everyone knows who you are! And what are those jingling johnnies you're carrying around?"

"They are slapsticks and bell rattles and jesters' scourges, if you please."

"And what's that fancy popinjay you've got there?"

"That's for learning parrot fashion."

"And what's that bundle of cotton wool for, there on the lead?"

"That is Johann the Carousel Horse, carefully packed in cotton wool."

"Fiddlesticks. What are you going to do with a carousel horse out here in the Libyan desert? Where did you get it from?"

"It's a sort of symbol, Mr Fireshine. Permit me to introduce ourselves. Here before you is the sterilised club of fantasts, 'The Blue Tulip.' "[46]

"I don't give a cuss for symbols. You've taken the horse away from its military duties. What's your name?"

"This chap's simply appalling!" said Jopp, "that's the purest robinsonade."

"Bosh," replied Borejay, "he's a fiction. That fellow Benjamin was at the back of it. He thinks it up and we're the ones to suffer . . ." "My dear Mr Fireshine! Your confederated salt-of-the-earthiness, your electuary coloration, doesn't impress us one bit. Nor your borrowed cinematics! But a word of explanation: we are fantasts. We no longer believe in intelligence. We have set out to save this animal, which commands our entire veneration, from the mob."

"I understand you," replied Fireshine, "but am quite unable to help you. Get into the paddy wagon. The horse, too. Forward march, make no ceremony about it. All aboard!"

Rosalie, the bitch, was ending her confinement. Five young police dogs saw the light of the world. Also around this time a Chinese kraken was caught in one of the Spree canals in Berlin. The creature was brought to the police station.

■ T H E ■ D E
C L I N E ■
A N D ■ F A L
L ■ O F ■ S
W A G G E R
P R A N C E ■

As his name implies, Swaggerprance [47] *is a being who loves sensations and makes a song and dance about things. He is one of those despairing types who, lacking any mental equilibrium, is unable to resist the slightest impression. Hence his tragic end. The author has placed particular emphasis on this. We see how Swaggerprance succumbs step by step first to obsession and then to a profound apathy. Until finally, after vain attempts to come up with an alibi, he sinks into that religiously coloured paralysis which, combined with excesses, seals his utter physical and moral ruin.*

And Swaggerprance suddenly felt a pressure on his temples. The productive currents that had warmed and enveloped his body were dying and hung like long saffron strips of wallpaper from his body. A gust of wind curled up his hands and feet. His back, a screeching turnscrew, soared to the sky in a spiral.

With a sneer, Swaggerprance seized a stone that was screaming from the corner of a building and defended himself blindly. Blue apprentices over-stormed him. A sky collapsed brightly. A ventilation shaft skewed. A chain of winged lying-in women flew across the sky.

The gasworks, the breweries and the domes of the town hall began to totter and resounded with a tympanic quacking. Brightly feathered demons spattered his brain, tousled and plucked it. Over the market square, which sank into the stars, towered the enormous sickle of a ship, its greenish hull standing vertically on its bow.

Swaggerprance stuck both index fingers into the vestibules of his ears and scraped out the last shabby remnants of the sun that had crept inside. Apocalyptic glory broke out. The blue apprentices sounded cowrie shells. They walked up balustrades of light and descended into the glory.

Swaggerprance was overcome by nausea. Gagging on the false god. He ran, flailing his arms in the air, tripped and fell on his face. A voice screamed out of his back. He closed his eyes and felt himself being hurled across the city in three enormous bounds. Suction pipes slurped the power from his mystical containers.

Swaggerprance fell to his knees, his chasuble a right pickle, and bared his teeth to heaven. House fronts are rows of graves stacked on high. Copper cities on the edge of the moon. Casemates which teeter on the tail of a shooting star by night. A pasted-on culture flakes off and is torn to shreds by vengeful spirits. Swaggerprance rages in a fit of St. Vitus's dance. One, two, one, two: means of mortifying the flesh. "Pan-catholicism," he screamed in his blindness. He sets up a General Consulate for Public Appeal and is the first to lodge a protest. He explains the obsessiveness of his excesses and hypnagogic monomanias in cinematic form. He is swirled around in a magnetic flask. He glows in the subterranean tubes of a sewer system. A beautiful scar adorns Swaggerprance's eye with white lustre.

He balances in a zigzag coloured shirt on the towering aether-spire. Then he hires enough momentum to clatter up and smash through the spokes of imaginary giant-wheels. He is threatened by the faces of Hasty Decision, Bustling Scalp and Carping Scepticism. The lobes of his lungs decimated, he hops out of the hand of a goblin.

His friends desert him. "Swaggerprance, Swaggerprance!" he crows from a mantelpiece. He plummets from the nexus. He drifts as a segment of a solar eclipse across the lopsided towers and domes of drunken cities. Sleepless and tucked into a little pram, he is pulled along the streets. The landscapes of blushing, sadness and bridal bliss overshadow him.

Swaggerprance witters on and concocts appropriate decadences. He deposits extensive anxiety complexes and orchestrates inhibitions in between — counterfeits of psychic cataracts and sensations. He curls up by night in a whore's body. His anxiety-skin stands on end behind his ears. "Are you saps trying to tell me — " and foaming from the mouth, he belches a blue cloud onto the floor. He crawls out into the sun. He craves the experience. Grass grows inauspiciously and drives him back into the dark. Curtains billow and a house floats away. The catalepsy of destruction. Tongues lash angularly at the paving-stones in a red rain of arrows.

Gagny, the leaden woman, must comb his parting so that he can muse. Dagny, the fishbride, looks after him, lit brightly by Musicon to her right. Swaggerprance had slain a captain[48] with a hymnal. He had invented an artificial floating island. He blunders into processions of supplicants and reveres vagabond-Jesus. He holds the lantern at requiems, and when he passes water: it is acetic clay.

But it does not help him. He is not up to these turbulences, detonations and radium fields. "Quantity is everything," he shouts, "syphilis is a serious venereal disease." He takes a bath in hydrochloric acid to rid himself of his feathered body. Remaining: one corn, a pair of gold spectacles, a set of false teeth and an amulet. And his soul, an ellipse.

Swaggerprance gave a bitter smile: "Originality is a blather infection. Painful and improbable. Commit murder. A murder is something that cannot be denied. Never! Create a rosy atmosphere. Always love the poor. We already have God as a supplement. Firm ground." And he blew on Musicon's neck: she disappeared in a cloud.

And he wrote his testament. With urine ink. He had nothing else. For he was in prison. There he cursed the fantasts, Dagny, Johann the Carousel Horse, his poor mother and many others. Then he died. A palm forest grew on a soda soup. A horse moved its legs and made headway. A flag of mourning fluttered over a hospital.

THE RED HEAVENS *A landscape of the upper inferno. A concert of frightful noises which astonishes even the animals. The latter appear partly as musicians (so-called cats' chorus) and partly in a state of taxidermy as props. The aunts from the seventh dimension participate in an obscene manner in the witches' Sabbath.*

The red heavens, mimul mahmi,
Are rent apart in agony,
The heavens plummet into the lake,
Mimulli mahmi, and have stomach ache.

The blue cats, fofolli mahmi,
Scratch a red-pointed metal sheet,
O lalalo lalalo lalaloo!
And now the aunt is purring there too.

The purring aunt lifts from the snow
Her warbling knickers and skirts to her throat.
O lalalo lalalo lalalo!
And the flutebuck said: "there you go."

The thundering tuba falls in the pit,
And double Johann jumps after it.
O lalalo and mimulli milin!
Two scrape away on the iron violin.

The horse and the donkey both turned a blind eye

As the snow lark below started to cry.
The turquoise tuba emitted a roar —
And everyone sang once four is four.

O lalalo lalalo lalay,
The head is of glass and the hands are of hay.
O lalalo lalalo laloo,
Flabberdegaz and hullabaloo!

```
■ S A T
A   N O
P O L
I S ■
```

A mystical event in the lowest ink-hell. Tenderenda relates the story before an audience of the deceased and of ghosts, of Satanopolitan initiates and habitués. He assumes previous knowledge of the persons present and of the locality, and a familiarity with subterranean institutions.

A journalist had got away. His grey figure overshadowed the pastures of Satanopolis. It was decided to launch an attack on him. The revolutionary tribunal was convened. They launched their attack on him, a grey figure who was frolicking about the meadows of Satanopolis. He was not to be found however. Although he had got up to all manner of mischief, he grazed contentedly and ate the prickly heads of the thistles that blossomed on the pastures of Satanopolis. Then his house was discovered. It stood on top of the 26½th hill, where the censer of the Holy Trinity is situated. They surrounded the house with cresset-lights. Their moonhorns shone pale in the night. Everyone advanced, bird-cages in their hands.

"That's a nice canid-swatter you've got there," said Mr Smith to Mr Brown. "The nit-picking effrontery of it!" replied Mr Jones to Mr Smith, who mounted his old nag, which was his infirmity, and rode off vexed.

Meanwhile a crowd of knitting guillotine-furies had gathered, and it was decided to take the journalist by storm. The house he occupied was called the Moonhouse. He had barricaded it with mattresses of aether waves and placed the censer on the roof so that he stood under the special protection of the heavens. He lived on calamus, kefir and candy. He was also surrounded by the corpses of the departed, which fell from the earth down his chimney in great numbers. So he could hold out comfortably for several weeks. This wasn't his big problem. He felt well and filled his time by studying the 27 different ways of sitting and spooking. His name was Lilienstein.[49]

A meeting was held in the Devil's town hall. The Devil entered with Kis de Paris and ridicule,[50] spoke a few gruff words and sang the part of Rigoletto. A voice from below yelled that he was a pompous nincompoop and should cease trying to kid them. Then they discussed whether to incinerate by dancing the house Lilienstein held with his pince-nez, or have it devoured by fleas and bugs.

The Devil on the balcony got an attack of the knee-shakes, and said: "Matat's[51] abdomen ends in a dagger. He has piled mattresses of aether waves in front of his house, and the Towers of Lies teeter about him on the blueness of their foundations. He has rubbed himself down with corpse fat and made himself immune. Return in your hordes, each with a drum on his belt. Perhaps . . . and may we be crowned with success." The Devil's wife was blonde, slender, blue. She remained by his side, seated on a she-ass.

And the people turned and marched back, singing to the drum. And they arrived back at the Moonhouse and saw the mattresses of aether waves and Lilienstein strolling about with all the lights on. And the smoke from his lunch rose up from the chimney.

And he had hung up a large sign, on which was written:

"Qui hic mixerit aut cacarit
Habeat deos inferos et superos iratos. [52]

(He hadn't made this up, that came from Luther.)

And a second sign, on which was written:

"He who is afraid, should gird himself with armour.
If it helpz, it helpz.
For long live the Scheblimini[53] and may he live on.
Sedet at dexteris meis. There's the rub."

That peeved them no end, I can tell you. And they did not know how to make Lilienstein leave. But they came up with an idea: they bombarded Lilienstein's house with houndwort and honey. So he had to leave. And they pursued him.

On the way he stumbled over the sleeping carts which stood on the street on account of the sleeping sickness. On the way he stumbled over the legs of Petroleum,[54] who was sitting on a corner rubbing his belly. On the way he stumbled over the booth of the tutelary goddess of abortions, who spewed out children and made the approximately 72 stars of Good and the 36 stars of Evil dance on long strings. And they pursued him.

An apoplexy writhes in sky-blue ribbons. Blue-thirsty dapple-greys creep along. If you have seen this phallus you have seen them all. He rushed past the ink-squid — the one which is learning Greek grammar and rides a velocipede. Past the light-towers and blast furnaces in which the corpses of dead soldiers blaze by night. And he got away.

A manifesto was read out in the Devil's beer-gardens. A reward of 6,000 francs was offered to any person who could produce reliable information on the whereabouts of Lilienstein, the journalist who had landed in Satanopolis, or give details that would lead to the monster's trail. It was read out to a chorus of trumpets. To no avail.

People had already forgotten him and were tending their affairs when he was discovered on the corso in Italy, where sky-blue horsies were being ridden and the ladies carried long-handled sunshades, for it was hot.

He was spotted on one of the ladies' sunshades, where he had built a nest upon which he was brooding. He bared his teeth and emitted a shrill, piercing: "Zirrizittig-Zirritig." But it was no use. The lady on whose sun-shade he was sauntering was tugged back and forth. She was accused, accosted and accursed. She was delivered a blow to her rear, for it was assumed she was an informer. Whereupon he fell from his nest along with his eggs, to a howl of joy.

But all they managed to do was to rip the paper suit from his body. He himself escaped, withdrawing to the girders of a railway-station hall, high above where the smoke lingers. It was patently obvious that he could not remain there for long.

And indeed, after five days he came down and was placed before the judge. He was a picture of woe. His face was black with soot and his hands were sullied by ink stains. In his trouser pocket was a revolver. In his breast pocket was, apart from his wallet, Ludwig Rubiner's *Handbook of riminal sychology*.[55] He continued to bare his teeth "Zirritig-Zirrizittig."

And the ink-squids came out of their holes and laughed. And the zacko-padores[56] came up and sniffed at him. And the magic dragons and sea-horses whizzed around above his head.

And he was put on trial: "For having ruined in grey garb the pastures of the mystics, and for creating a stir by various forms of mischief." But the Devil became his advocate and defended him. "Calumnies and indolence," said the Devil, "what do you want from him? Behold, a man. Shall I wash my hands of guilt, or is he to be flayed?" And the poor and the beggars leapt forth and called out: "Lord, help us, we have fever." But he pushed them back with the flat of his hand and said: "Please, afterwards." And the trial was adjourned.

But the next day a large crowd returned, bringing razors and crying: "Away with him. He has blasphemed against God and the Devil. He is a journalist. He has besmirched our Moonhouse and built a nest on a lady's parasol."

And the Devil said to Lilienstein. "Defend thyself." And a gentleman seated among the spectators raised his voice and called out: "This gentleman has no connection with the action."[57]

And Lilienstein fell to his knees, entreated the stars, the moon and the crowd, and shouted: "Autolax is the best. Funnel-shaped suppositories woven from softwood and raffia were already known to antiquity. The Soxlet apparatus[58] is a modern day invention. The best laxative is Autolax. It is made from plant extracts. Do you hear: plant extracts! It need scarcely be mentioned that it is made by German industry," he stammered in his plight. "Take this remedy, I beseech you, and in return, let me go. What have I done that you should pursue me so? Behold, I am King of the Jews."

This was greeted by uncontrollable laughter. And the Devil said: " 'Sblood! Is this possible?" And the gentleman shouted from the audience: "Crucify him, crucify him!"

And he was sentenced to eat up all his dainty self-spun nonsense. And the devil-painter[59] Meideles did his portrait before he was handed over to the knacker. And all the flags dripped scorn and caustic remarks.

III.

```
■ G R A N
D ■ H O T
E L ■ M E
T A P H Y
S I C S ■
```

The birth of Dadaism. Mulche-Mulche, the quintessence of the fantastic, gives birth to young Mr Foetus high above in that region which, surrounded by music, dance, foolishness and divine familiarity, distinguishes itself quite clearly from its opposite.

None of Messrs Clemenceau's and Lloyd George's speeches, nor Ludendorff's [60] gunshots, prompted as much uproar as the small fluctuating bunch of Dadaistic itinerant prophets as they preached childishness after their own fashion.

Mulche-Mulche made her way to the observation roof of the Grand Hotel Metaphysics in an elevator made of tulips and hyacinths. Up above, awaiting her were: the Master of Ceremonies, whose duty it was to arrange the astronomical instruments; Clague-ass, who was greedily regaling himself with a bucket full of raspberry squash; and Musicon, Our Lady, constructed solely out of passacaglias and fugues.

Mulche-Mulche's slender leg was completely wrapped in chrysanthemums, so that she could only take a modest step when walking. Her rose-petal tongue fluttered briefly between her teeth. Golden rain hung from her eyes and the black counterpane of the four-poster which had been prepared for her was painted with silver hounds.

The hotel was made of rubber and was porous. The gables and eaves of the upper storeys jutted out far over the front. Once Mulche-Mulche was undressed and the sparkle of her eyes had coloured the heavens — hooee, Clague-ass had already drunk his fill. Hooee, he shouted his welcome with a voice that was audible far and wide. The Master of Ceremonies gave a number of deep bows and edged the telescope towards the parapet in order to study the celestography. However Musicon — a golden flame dancing incessantly round the four-poster — suddenly raised her arms, and behold, violins rained shadows across the city.

Mulche-Mulche's eyes blazed. Her body was stuffed full with corn, incense and myrrh so that the bed covers rose and bulged. The freight inside her belly was increased by all manner of fruit and seed, until it burst the wraps in which it was bound with a crack.

At this the entire rachitic populace[61] of the neighbourhood set about hindering a birth which threatened their barren land with fertility.

P.T. Bridet, the flower of death tucked in his hat, swelled on his wooden leg, crying blue murder. A poisonous smile[62] had embossed itself across his chops. He raced up grimly from the parlour of the departed, ready to deal angrily with this unheard of business.

And then came Pimperling with his unscrewable head. The tympanic membranes hung crumpled from his ears on both sides. He wore a head-band of Northern Lights, latest model. Specimen of the mud-swamped mass-graver who, coated with vanilla and incensed by the rat he smelt, set about safeguarding his good odour.

And then came Toto, who had nothing apart from his name. His steely Adam's apple purred smoothly in the wind when he walked into the nor'-easter. He had girded his Jericho stomacher[63] about his waist so the fluttering rags of his guts would not get lost. The Marseillaise, his Shobboleth, shone crimson from his chest.

And they besieged the gardens, posted sentries and shot at the roof terrace with big guns from the movie world, thundering day and night. They sent the violet-radiating "Potato-soul" floating upwards as a sounding balloon. "God save the King" or "The family that prays together stays together" was inscribed upon their signal rockets. And they had "We are being consumed by our fear of the present" shouted up at the terrace through a megaphone. At that moment the deity up above was busying his fingers trying vainly to lure young Mr Foetus from out of Mulche-Mulche's rumbling body. He was already taking a cautious peep out of the gaping maternal portal. But he withdrew with a blink of his cunning fox face on seeing the four of them, Jopp, Musicon, Deity and Clague-ass, assembled to receive him with butterfly nets, sticks and staves and a wet face flannel. And haughty squirts and spurts of sweat gushed from Mulche's reddened body, sousing everything far and wide.

The people were in a quandary as to what to do with their rusted film artillery, and as to whether they should clear off or stay. They asked the advice of the "Potato-soul" and decided to storm the charming scene at the Grand Hotel Metaphysics with violence.

They rolled up the first of the catapults — the Idol of Fashion. This is a low-browed pin-head which sparkles under its burden of rhinestones and oriental gewgaws. It can be called the Funless Idol because it has been carved from head to foot out of wooden fibs and wears an iron heart on its chest as a watch fob.

Black-throated and bedecked with bells, it towers up with the tuning fork of vice held on high in its right hand. Although it is painted over and over with characters from the Qabbalah and the Talmud, it stares quite affably from its childish pupils. Its six hundred self-swivelling arms twist both facts and history. It also has a tin box with an oxy-hydrogen blowpipe fixed to its hindmost vertebra. And so the unguentary evacuation takes place; the scarcely human forms of generals and gang leaders are expelled abaft and their faces get dragged through the filth.

But Jopp, aided by Musicon, lowers the fuse into the depths of its stomach and, since it is loaded with hespar, salfurio, acunite and vitriol,[64] they blow it up and thwart the assault.

The second idol, the "Bearded Dog," is wheeled up in order to wash away the tender anecdotes from the terrace of the Grand Hotel Metaphysics, with its primordial roars and rancour. The bedrock of religions is prized up with crow-bars, so as to open up a way and a path. "Ideological Superstructure" shares fall rapidly. "Oh no, the descent into bestiality!" Bridet whines. "The magic printing works of the Holy Ghost can no longer halt this decline."

It was already hissing up, coupled in front of a church on castors — worried priests, prelates, deacons and the *Summi Episcopi* keeping look-out behind its curtains. Five-ridged back bones drag along its mangy hide, which had been tattooed with troops. Its receding brow crowned with the likeness of Golgotha. Up until now it had remained in the stable of allegories, fed with a chaff made of lines of force. Now it is rolled up to puff its astonishment at Musicon's melodious voice.

But its rage outdoes itself. Before its breath can reach the ridge of the roof, it arches its back and sheds the seeds of its manhood, which smell of jasmine and water lilies. Enfeebled, the monster's knees tremble. It lays its head on its paws, whimpering submissively. With a lash of its own tail it demolishes the wobbly holiday church belonging to the public guardians who had been pulling it. And thus this onslaught also failed.

And while Musicon's golden flame dances along the airy observation roof, umbala oh-oh,[65] the last idol is brought up: Puppet Death made of stucco, stretched out lengthways in the truck ready to be hoisted up on its strings. "Long live scandal!" called Pimperling in greeting. "Poetic friend," said Toto, "there is a sick mutilated corpse about thy head.[66] Thine eyes are coloured cobalt blue, thy forehead pale ochre yellow. Hand me the suit-case. Selah." And Bridet: "Verily, most discreet master, thine odour is not so bad for thine age. This is going to be tremendous fun. May each shake a leg which he hath torn from the other. Let us build a triumphal arch, and where thou placest thy foot, mayest thou be accompanied by joy and well-being!"

With that Death gave a nod and took their experiences from them in the way one accepts a letter of submission, then offering his head to the noose which was to convey him to the roof. They hooked the bobbins on to him, turned the handles and guided him up. But the load was too heavy. He had reached three quarters of the way, swinging and swaying and livening to the prospect of scaling the roof ridge. The ropes tautened, whistled and sang, the hawser screeched, and he crashed down from the dizzying heights, landing with all his weight on Pimperling who, honest to the core, had expected anything but such a bump. Thrice dead and five times slain, they wrapped him in a handkerchief, carried him to one side and feverishly attempted to pull the dislodged timberwork of the rear of his head back into place. But there was no helping him. And even Death was split asunder during Pimperling's death by Death.

Then Mulche-Mulche suddenly let out twelve piercing screams in quick succession. Her compass-leg rose to the edge of the sky. And she gave birth. First a small Jewish boy[67] wearing a tiny coronet on his purple brow, who at once swung up onto the umbilical cord and started to perform gymnastics. And Musicon laughed, as if she were his cousin.

And forty days passed, which Mulche spent with chalky countenance by the parapet. Then she raised her compass-leg a second time, high into the sky. And this time she gave birth to a large quantity of dishwater, scree, rubble, mud and lumber which showered, rattled and thundered over the parapet and squashed the plantigrades' lust and limbs. Jopp was pleased with this, and Deity lowered his butterfly net and looked on in amazement.

And another forty days passed and Mulche stood lost in thought and with large devouring eyes. Then she raised her leg a third time and gave birth to Mr Foetus, as described in Folio 28, Ars magna. Confucius had praised him. A shiny border adorns his back. His father is Plimplamplasko,[68] the lofty spirit, addicted to miracles and drunk with love.

```
■ B U L B O'
S ■ P R A Y E
R ■ A N D
■ T H E ■
R O A S T ■
P O E T ⁶⁹ ■
```

The laughter increases to the same degree as the horror. Contrasts become glaring. Death has taken on a magical form. On the other hand, life, light and joy are defended very consciously. The *forces* majeures *enter the cupboards in* person. God dances against death.

Now one might imagine that death himself had died, but far from it. Scarcely had the great ghosts started to intone the dirge on their cement pipes than Death, elevated and set in motion by this rhythm, reappeared in person and began a lively dance on iron legs. Fists clenched inwards, he stamped and hammered the floor with thundering hoofs.

And the great ghosts laughed, and the coffin lids of their cheek-bones cracked. For the Great Death had returned. Thereupon Bulbo sank to his knees, threw his arms up to the heavens and shouted:

"Save us, O Lord, from this enchantment. Pull, O Lord, our besotted mouths out of the muckpails, runnels and cesspits which we are so stuck on. O Lord, have pity on our sojourn in this stew, this latrine. Our ears are bandaged with iodoform gauze, the flock of wine porters and leather-jackets graze on the lobes of our lungs. We have landed up in the realm of threadworms and false gods. The call to salvation is gaining the upper hand.

"They beat your archangels with fiery staffs. They entice your angels to earth and make them fat and useless. They roll their drunks into your promised land at the point where hell borders paradise, and the Wagnerian yodel rings out, wigalaweia, *in Germano panta rei*.[70]

"Your Church has become a place of ridicule, a bawdy-house. They call us blasphemers and pestilential Gnostics. But their apaches and bestial faces appear behind their wealth of flesh. How can one love them? The number of found foetuses multiplies in the drawers, and the chubby tyke loafs about in the beds.

"They no longer see the mummy in the hammock, the rubble of embalmed limbs and the cholera bacilli in the seam of the bull fiddle. No longer the gruel which drips from the flue, nor the family father with his putrefied feelings. No sooner are they in the womb than they sell each other their eternal life.

"They embezzle the wheat flour intended for your Holy Host, and oil their tonsils with the plonk which should represent your Holy Blood. But you forgive our wickedness, just as we also promise to do our part.

"I could even live in a different era. But what use would that be to me, O Lord? Look, I am deliberately putting down roots among these people. As a professional starver I nourish myself on asceticism. But the theory of relativity is not enough, nor the philosophy of "as if".[71] Our pamphlets no longer have any effect. The symptoms of galloping marasmus multiply. All the sixty million souls of my people gush out of my pores. It is but rat-sweat before you, my Lord. So save us, help us, pneumatic father!"

Then a black branch sprang from Bulbo's mouth: Death. And the poet was cast into the midst of the ghosts. And Death danced, then marched upon him.

But the Lord spake: "*Mea res agitur*.[72] He champions an aesthetics of sensory associations which are connected to ideas. A moral philosophy in literary grotesques. His doctor's stuff is pleasing to the ear." And he decided to dance as well, for the prayer had pleased him.

Then God danced with this righteous soul against Death. Three archangels provided his hair-do with a tower-high toupee. And Leviathan hung his hind-parts over the wall of heaven and looked on. But the tower-high crown, woven from the prayers of the Israelites, wobbled on the summit of the Lord's hair-do.

And a whirlwind sprang up, and the Devil crept into his secret chamber behind the dancing-ground and yelled: "Grey sun, grey stars, grey apple, grey moon." The sun, stars, apple and moon fell on the dancing-ground. Whereupon the ghosts consumed them.

Then the Lord said: "Aulum babaulum, fire!" And sun, stars, apple and moon shot up from the bowels of the ghosts and resumed their places.

Then Death teased God, saying: *"Ecce homo logicus!"* and flew to the uppermost step. And opened his grand bazoo to demonstrate his authority.

Then God hit him over the head with the table of categories so that it shattered, and continued dancing with manly flourishes and nimble twirls. Death however crunched the table of categories underfoot, whereupon the ghosts consumed it.

Then Death made a rain of ashes from the ragout of wood shavings intended for the coffins, and shouted: *"Chaque confrère une blague, et la totalité des blagues: humanité,"* cracking the coffin lids of his cheek-bones by way of accompaniment. And the shavings descended on all sides, whereupon the ghosts devoured them.

Then God lowered his trumpet and shouted: *"Satana, Satana, ribellione!"* [73] And thereupon the man in red appeared, his false majesty, and slayed Death, such that no one could recognise him henceforth. Whereupon the ghosts devoured him.

But lo, they grew very powerful and shouted: "We're being served a roast poet!"

"Cow, thou art ours!" said the Devil.

"Liberty, fraternity, heaven – thou art ours."

"Ourness and sourness," said the Devil, "what's this all supposed to mean?"

Then the Lord handed them the roast poet. Whereupon the ghosts squatted in a circle, removed his shoots and peeled off his crust and feather-down and consumed him. It turned out that his trouser buttons were consecrated wafers, his larynx unfermented, his brain fragrant, but his navel askew. And the youngest ghost delivered the funereal oration:

"This was a psychofact,"[74] he began, "not a person. Hermaphrodite from head to toe. His spiritual shoulders stuck sharply through the gussets of his cutaway. His head a magic onion of intellectuality. Blindly commanded by the urge to confess ceaselessly, his beginnings, his start and finish were of such virginal, such utterly uncompromising mental hygiene that we who follow in his wake are unable to integrate our doubts on the obligation to revolutionary, morally improving motherhood, into our as yet feeble aspirations towards a cosmos of will to flight and overcoming the earth, as an indispensible yet sweet problem within the tragedy.

"Glorious things lie buried here beneath a tangle of unripened rhetoric that remains abstract. Subjectivistic ecstatics were not always able to escape being a theatrical end in themselves. A sturdy zealot and fakir-like seeker of salvation, high priest and seer, fountain-head and spurrer of dithyrambic impulses, the sole fact that sadly impairs his laudable example is that Max Reinhardt,[75] whose creative staging enriched the outlines of individual visions, was only able to give the expert his expertise long after the former's departure. *Requiescat in pace.*"

And they consumed him; and likewise they consumed the orator. And they consumed the plates. And they consumed the forks. And likewise the dancing-ground. Oh, it was just as well that the Lord had already departed from the scene. They would have consumed him, too.

There is nothing more to be said. But possibly a little more could be sung. "Thou magic quadrate, now it's too late." That's an address from one who knows the meaning of silence. "Ambrosian steer": by which is meant the Ambrosian song of praise. A turn towards the Church is revealed in the vocabulary and vowels. The hymnus begins with military reminiscences and concludes with an invocation to Solomon, that great magus who consoled himself by taking the Egyptian King's daughter to his heart. The Egyptian King's daughter is Magic.

```
■ H Y
M N U
S ■ I ■
```

Thou lord of the birds, dogs and cats, of spirits and bodies, of spooks and dingbats,

Thou above and below, by the right, by the left, straight on, about turn and halt,

The spirit is in thee and thou art in it, and you are in you and we are in us.

Thou art resurrected, who once was vanquished.

The unbound one who tore his chains,

The almighty art thou, the all-nightly, most knightly, with a burning pot on your pate.

The thunder in thy box has exploded in all directions and languages.

Thy tin-neck towers and thy spoke soars, in reason and unreason, in the realms of the quick and the dead.

Thou camest with mighty roars, basinet of rebellion, crowing-trumpet, son of the earth.

In fiery chasms and the bullets' hail, in dying whimpers and endless curses,

In clouds of printer's ink, communion wafers and cakes, and countless blasphemous verses.

So we beheld thee, so we held thee, in a rain of faces carved from agate.

On toppled thrones, ruptured cannon, on tatters of newspaper, foreign notes and shares,

Gaily adorned dolly, thou hast held the sword of justice above the doctrinaires.

Thou God of maledictions and sewers, demon prince, God of the possessed.

Thou mannequin with violets, garters, perfumes and painted with a whore's face.

Thy seven kooks are cocking snooks, thy great aunts are miscreants, thy headgear's a red sphere.

Thou prince of sickness and remedy, Father of the Bulbos and Tenderendae,

Of arsenics and salvarsans,[76] gas taps, soaped nooses and booby traps,

Thou undoer of all ties, casuist of every twist and turn,

Thou God of lamps and candelabras, thou nourishest thyself on light cones, triangles and stars.

Thou torture wheel, Ferris wheel of pain, homocentaurus, thou sailest in winged trousers through the sick bay.

Thou wood, copper, bronze, zinc, gable and mast, an iron bell, thou whirrest smoothly past.

Thou magic quadrate, now it's too late, thou mystic *quartier*, Ambrosian steer,

Lord of our denudation, thy five fingers are the foundation of our salvation.

Lord of our dog Latin and hunter's cant, lamentotympani of our existence, eternalist, communist, Antichrist, Oh! most sagacious sagacity of Solomon!

Thou who hast pushed our maids of honour, our posies and perfumeries and our intoxicating drugs to one side,

We greet thee with bombards, pipes and chimes, with ringing cymbals and torrents of words.

Thou who hast cast our mooncalves, our cook-books and astrologies onto the streets,

Who hast cried out with the voice of ten thousand changelings,

Who drew near and made his entry, laughing kite and triumphator,

We greet thee with promissory notes, tin, enamel, paper and pin money.

Thou who holdest in custody scrofulous children and zebras in the cheek pouches of thy behorned head,

The dallying poet, the passionate pleb, the newspaperman and the priest have offered themselves up for a Mark.

Pierce our noses with the ring of thine omnipotence, place a fence in our jaws and bridle our splendour.

We make a great song and dance in raiments of rags and paper, of window glass, tar-board and cement.

We swing our pan-Germanic crab-sticks, painted with runes and swastikas.

Thy kingdom stretcheth from the navel to the knees, and the Lutheran codfish barks.

Save us, O Lord, from the persecutions of the heretics and utopians, the Fiend and prophets.

Save us, O Lord, from the conceits of the theoreticasters and liturgists, from the united bell-ringers.

Lead us, O lord, from this land of duty-bugs, of cold damp cakes and towns cobbled with death certificates.

Cease thy beating on wood, copper, bronze, ivory, stone and thine other mighty drums.

Cease parading our dead before our eyes and disturbing our warmth, O Lord, we pray thee.

Cease placing the ghosts on our table, the ghosts in our coffee cups, and the incubi will stop rustling in the stair joists.

THE PUTREF ACTION CONDUCTOR [77]

It is assumed in this chapter that a merchant butcher will be the last to be buried. Later, however, a number of others prove to have outlived the Great Death. The mourners are revenants and three month-old corpses. The funeral develops into a festive procession similar to those celebrated at the Eleusinian Mysteries. To the right of the scene, a darkness that is felt to be oppressive is packed into crates. To the left, a poetry club which has also survived proves to be eagerly involved in recording the putrefaction and in watering down the fantastic reality appropriately.

Everyone had just reached an agreement when the putrefaction conductor handed in his letter of resignation. It was on the day that the last funeral took place. All the departed had assembled. They suppressed their smell as best they could, fastened their jaws tight and handed round perfume. The horse cadaver, which was to draw the hearse, was draped with a vestment so that its worm-ridden nudity would not appear too blatant.

And the master of ceremonies of the gloomy proceedings lifted up his voice and read aloud from the programme:

"God, the almighty,
has found pleasure,
in summoning our ancestor, grandmother, mother and child,
Mr Godfrey Toothgap,
from the firm Toothgap, Jawbone & Co.,
Meat and Sausage Wholesaler,
to Him."

"Today be 'ee depahrtid, depahrtid be 'ee," the choir boomed.

"The deceased departed in exemplary fashion. He was always a devoted servant of the Church. His departure is accompanied by the declaration of our lewd commiseration, the deeply felt pain-ovation of his friends and relatives, who, recognising the dodgy situation in time, cleared off before him. It just remains to be added that the sausage factory, which now lies idle, was summoned to life beforehand under the direction of the departed."

With that the funeral procession set off on its way, and the putrefaction conductor ascended the platform and conducted for the last time. And his amanuensis produced the thunder on a baking tray. And the words of the Corybants could be heard as the odorous procession disappeared down the streets:

"He who landed on the quay by night,
Hardest boiled and looking a fright,
With his beard, and his petrified
Leather wallet, he'd travelled world-wide —
He who slaughtered sheep and pig,
Played gay blade, jiggety-jig,
Pushed his goods and pushed himself,
Raised his prices and sunk his wealth —
Perhaps his poor fool's soul now fears,
That the dividends are in arrears.
Does he blush in his mind's eye?

He's finished up now high and dry."

And the parson raked the remains in the coffin into a pile with the church cross, whilst the amanuensis thundered and the putrefaction conductor conducted:

"Mourners, bring him over here,
Laid out flat upon his bier,
And let the corpse of this go-getter
Sup its fill and feel much better.
Place him on the heavenly square,
Wrapped from head to toe in shares.
Lace his shirt with care, I beg,
He's climbing out his trouser leg.
Imperial Eagle ink allays,
The reddened rims around his eyes.
And may all that he's amassed till now,
Float above his weary brow."

Lo, the sacristans of the lower heavens had assembled to the right. Wearing cowls of tolerant cashmere and tall caps of ashes, they were busy packing as much of the solar eclipse as they could into crates. For the air was thick with it and gave people headaches. And some of these servants of the cloth were bare-headed. Their tin eyes squinted. Whenever they bent their heads the wind caught in the tinder of their hair and made it rattle.

But to the left the "Buxom Leg" poetry club had set up its vibration machines, gigantic catapults with which the putrefaction and the minutest vibrations of the inner life could be registered and calculated.

But they also had the washing machine of banalisation[78] in tow; reality was stuffed into its neck and rendered valueless by means of cogwheels and whisks. And as the darkness dazzled everyone's eyes, some took the opportunity to display a depraved eroticism. They hauled together mud, mortar and stones and baked a gigantic vulva, the sex of the goddess Ta-hu-re.[79]

Then the putrefaction conductor raised his arms three notches higher, motioned to the heated pursuits and said: "Give me the names and birth-places of these people."

And the amanuensis raised the baking tray as a black sun and said: "Show forbearance, Sire, they are idealists. Thou seest it in the ardour of their inner life. They are born of the twilight and have forgotten to die. Now they're poetising for the naked point."

And the putrefaction conductor raised his arms yet three notches higher, blew his nose, spat to the right and the left, and said: "Are there any decadents among them, transcendental decadents?"

"No," said the amanuensis, "just some night-revellers who are climbing up the monument to Gleim,[80] that great man of poetry, and spoiling the view."

And the putrefaction conductor took a closer look and said: "They seem to be full of activity."

"Yes, Sire," said the amanuensis, "they are very involved in their antics." By which he was referring to the washing machine of banalisation. But at that moment one of the many club members left the sphere of influence, drew nearer, held out an offertory box and yelled: "Humanity in word and writing! Humanity gratis!" And others jostled round him, wringing out the wet cloths they had bound round their heads, and reciting the maxims and jests they had just made up.

The one: "Starbrows of my martyr-crown," and "Lantern-king from Jerusalem." The next: "I would just like to point out: as soon as you step up the steep stairs . . . stare up the steep stets . . . stet up the stair steets . . ." The third: "Tap tap, my asthma, drive off, you carriage" and: "The great abscesses glow behind our brows."

"Sire, thou exaggeratest," said the amanuensis. "Basically they're a harmless crowd. They do not deserve thy wrath."

But as one of them at the back, next to the scaffolding, smoked his pipe and began to read out his essay: "On the Beauty of Unlaid Eggs," the putrefaction conductor was seized with impatience and shouted: "You are all coarse, uncouth and provocative. You think you're too good to work by the sweat of your brows. You want a place in the sun. Give them a penny for their collection and a penny for the man who is playing the dirge on his windpipe. Serpent, shoo them out of their holes. It pains me to see them seated there like that."

They protested at this. And disheartened, the amanuensis said: "They just want to remain seated here and devour their cerebral cortices. That's all.

And they no longer have their trews. They have even sacrificed the shirts on their backs."

"Toss them Abdul Hamid's[81] brown trousers!" the master said in resignation, "and let's be off. There's no helping them. Verily, if their tempers were to get heated they might end up threatening to thrust a sabre into our guts because we're not prepared to buy up their experiences. My God, what a foolhardy breed!"

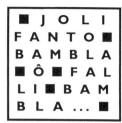

Depiction of an elephant caravan from the inter-nationally ill-famed cycle "gadji beri bimba." The author presented this cycle for the first time in 1916 as a novelty at the Cabaret Voltaire. The bishop's costume of glossy paper he wore for the occasion, as well as the towering, blue and white bestriped shaman's hat, are revered to this day as fetishes by the gentle inhabitants of Haway.

jolifanto bambla ô falli bambla[82]
grossiga m'pfa habla horem
égiga goramen
higo bloiko russula huju
hollaka hollala
anlogo bung
blago bung
blago bung
bosso fataka
ü üü ü
schampa wulla wussa ólobo
hej tatta gôrem
eschige zunbada
wulubu ssubudu ulu wassubada
tumba ba-umf
kusa gauma
ba-umf

Tenderenda, for his part, passes the homage on to the *discreet head of his order. In this hymnus the forefather of the hymnologists is given, among others, the names "Chaldaean archangel," "Coral of the Beyond" and "Fluid Master." The carnival of fools constituted by this little booklet is offered up to him: "We grimacers, dancing round the water butt in cloaks of fire." Most especially the last verses reveal a total surrender. Tenderenda has been seized by a great home-sickness. He recites the verses out loud in bleak moments for his edification.*

Chaldaean Archangel, Aster King, purple
Man with the hands which spell sleep,
Thou lettest the animals appear within us,
Thou pinnest us to the jingling medals of the Magician,
Thou linkest us with the stars,
Which slice and divide us up.
Master of all saints, of all the dead,
Alembic in which we faded,
We die crosswise and lengthwise,
The final cough racks us,
We sink down into the infinite space, Laurentius-
Tears,[83] radiant and zealous.

Thou Zone Chief, black Chief,
How addicted we are to seizures,
How seized by addiction to death!
The holy doctor Kosmas cannot help us.

We die to thee now and then, we die to thee completely.
In thee art all things united.
We carry the Great Bear in our arms as an ulcer,
A sun of *Terra siena* in our hearts.
Possessing in thy possession, we free ourselves.

We pinked trumpets, fluttering in the crystal wind,
We tragic peacocks, shattering on every step,
We grimacers, dancing round the water butt in cloaks of fire,
Thou girdle of stars, thou spherical wall, rolling darkness.
Thou oriental people, occidental people,
War marches muttering in minor keys, froth on the Tower of thy Grace.[84]

Thou Cymbalum Mundi, Coral of the Beyond, Fluid Master,
Loud weepeth the scale of man and beast.
Loud lamenteth the people of the cities of fire and smoke.
And thine enchanted horns appeared as thou beholdest thy fictile play-
things, as thou inspectest thy realm and us, the administrators of thy
cadastre.
For the rouge cracked. For the dice decomposed.
For never was there such sin as here.

Thou countenance pieced together from metaphors,
Carnival-poem-puppet
Of our fears. Thou scent of white paper!
Paper, ink, writing implements and cigarettes,
We leave everything behind. Subdued, we follow thee.

Our feet free themselves from the figures that were instilled in us,
A sweet stream flows forth from the liquors which were distilled in us.
We exchange the rare for cash, the fair for balderdash.
One item for three, the city of night for Varanasi.

 *Unvarnished outburst or expectoration from the eponymous hero. The author calls him a fantast, whereas Tenderenda calls himself "church poet" in his high-flown fashion. He also calls himself the "Knight of Glossy Paper," which points to the Quixotic array in which Tenderenda liked to disport himself during his life. He admits to being tired of his cheerfulness, and supplicates Heaven's blessing. The phrasing of the Benediction deserves special praise, for its merry inflections are highly apt for Tenderenda's heaven-tripping nature. He might be taken for an exorcist because he brings chimeras to his stable. The persecutions of the Devil, which are hinted at in the* benedicite, *are those phantasmata which St. Ambrosius[85] had already complained about, and whose abjuration another saint named as a precondition for entry into monkhood. Otherwise Tenderenda's state is elegiac and he shies away from the masses. The wordplays, miracles and adventures have worn him down. He longs for peace, quietude and Latin abstraction.*

It commenced with a rumble: Laurentius Tenderenda, the church poet, a hallucinade in three parts. Laurentius Tenderenda, or the crazed trancelator of inevitability. Laurentius Tenderenda, the primal essence of the astral cannonade. That was intended as a nice monkey-trick for easily delighted diaphragms. But it ended in a tragedy for good common sense, and gullibility on the part of the fashionable ninnies and word flagellants.

A prayer book manufacturer[86] spoke the prologue, and the theatre rocked beneath the whirligig of the multitude. The gables were fastened with hat-pins, and from the balconies hung the hungry tape-worms, elomen.[87] This

Goliath's amenable body was opened, and ten storeys toppled out. The rattlesnakes were taken to the turret and the buck's horn was blown for afternoon tea.

Oh this century of incandescent light and barbed wire, primal energy and abyss! What use here were documents on torture? Before a people of warriors, before the assembled chorus of poetry editors? Laurentius Tenderenda, or the missionary among the sweatfoots and redskins of the Academy for Physical Instruction. A Book of Concord and a tower of coughing. I want to deliver nicely fattened material. I'm not one for arm-chair skirmishes. If only it wasn't for this constant death rattle of sulphuretted chloride. Not another step, or I'll give my last gasp.

Now they have left to set their three-seater donkey at a gallop. Garnets, lemon and Venetian blue smoke of their pointy hats. Now the hen broods at High Mass, and they chase after her with the offertory bag. They boil their pocket watches in calamine lotion and paint over Nostradamus with heliotrope.

For me that's the purest satanic perfumery. It also smells slightly of black stew and spiked wire. But in the second section the mourners will gird themselves with sayings from the Koran as stomachers. Art as the buckle. Burlesque sermon in three instalments. Or the encyclopaedic prayer-cylinder. Or the inscrutable searching look into the infernal world of mustachioed ribaldry.

I'd be a right one if I didn't grasp that. A right one if I was unwilling to set about the beast with boot-jacks. The female ideal of the German people does not reside in the public houses of pleasure. The cockatoo has fallen into the poison. The Blue Rider is not a Red Biker.[88] And I thought I'd sealed the matter in bottles once and for all.

They have placed the ink-squid on my bed. And handed me the roots of their teeth to eat. I have imbibed valerian and rubbed down the church spire with emery paper. And I do not know whether I belong to those above or those down below. For the unbelievable, ne'er conceivable comes to pass here.

Without any preamble: by nature I am a child of passion. My *mons pubis* stands comparison. Forty days I lay in bicarb. The teeth of the godless will grow long in their jaws.

I could recite the psalms of penitence and make the sign of the Holy Cross. Who would that help? I could anoint my locks with the oil of sunflowers and pluck the Davidian harp? *Cui bono?* [89] Portraying the stock-exchange bulls and master dyers of the New Jerusalem: of what use would that be to me?

This is the eleventh and last of the parabases. The knight of glossy paper is tired of his cheerfulness. The organ has eased his departure. The chimeras have been brought to the stable, and the Church Father Origen basks his bald pate in the setting sun. O Lord, may eternal seeds give us a good Cordial Medoc, and the orchestra of thrice-beaked hookahs fall silent for a moment.

Benedicat te Tenderendam, dominus, et custodiat te ab omnibus insidiis diaboli [90]. O Huelsenbeck, O Huelsenbeck, *quelle fleur tenez-vous dans le bec?* [91] The roots copulate in the shrines. Detectives are our cockades, and we say the "gadji beri bimba" as our bedtime prayer.

Tenderenda who makes the sign of the cross, they'll call me. They will display my bones on the *Sedia gestatoria*.[92] They'll sprinkle holy water over me. They'll call me a full-blown monk of preservation and filtering-cloth for impurities. Ass-king and schismaticaster. *In nomine patris et filii et spiritus sancti.*

A good thing though that my Pentecostal mood remains undisturbed by over-crass outsiders. A good thing that I can keep in good form. If I had a notebook to hand, or were something else to proffer itself, I would write down more of what I call to mind. For I recall the whole period. It is a mighty falling and recalling which I wish to hold onto with faltering callowness.

A magic incantation from the "gadji beri bimba" cycle mentioned earlier. It is dedicated to Tenderenda's two mystic animals, the peacock and the cat. Two proud and taciturn beasts, the Jeremiah and mourning woman among the animals. It is recommended to speak it casually and not to dwell on it too long. It has been conceived of simply as a kind of bridge to link the two last prose texts.

baubo sbugi ninga gloffa[93]
siwi faffa
sbugi faffa
ôkofa
fafâmo
faufo halja finj

sirgi ninga banja sbugi
halja hanja golja biddin

mâ mâ
piaûpa
mjâma

pâwapa
baungo
sbugi
ninga
gloffâlor

An astral fairy tale. A kind of heavenly puppet play. 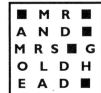 *Three sections can clearly be distinguished. The first: the Goldheads have a mystic experience. A white avalanche comes to visit them, a constantly growing purity and brightness stretches towards them. Their house is situated above the abyss and on the fabulous meadow* on which the alphabet tree wanders. This is the tree from which the poetic Adams and Eves eat. Gentle allegories appear in animal form. Dreamlike — the music-stands[94] of laughter which Tenderenda distributed during his life. The second section is the Ballad of Koko the Green God.[95] That is the god of the fantasts. All bliss and contentment emanates from him, so long as he beats his wings in freedom. But placed in confinement he avenges himself by casting spells on those closest to him. The third section is an epilogue for the Goldheads. It shakes the dust of its times from its feet and prophesies the end of the godless and of bewitchment. The last stroke is performed, as is meet and just, by a verse from the Prince of Poets, Johann von Goethe.

Mr and Mrs Goldhead meet on the blue wall. Mr Goldhead has a shooting star hanging from his nose. Mrs Goldhead has a green feather duster in her hat-band. Mr Goldhead bows and scrapes. Mrs Goldhead has a hand like a five-pronged fork.

An avalanche comes up the stairs. Hard on the heels of the night. A white avalanche up the wobbly stairs. Mrs Goldhead curtseys. Mr Goldhead taps his brow. A white fountain gushes from his head. The likes of this had never been seen. Not in this or any other century.

The fire- and snow-cocks fly up from the depths, appalled. The rasping cows wipe each other's noses. The alphabet tree strolls on the emerald meadow. On the emerald meadow: soda-soap worm jiggets on the rein. Its rider falls off and distributes the music-stands of laughter. He boards the morning and evening swing, rocks and sways and hops into the beyond. Then the flutebuck, tumblebuck and tulipbuck arrive, craning their necks. In the background there is a birdhouse. Sitting inside is the caduda cock, foaming stars.

Mr Goldhead, astonished: "The tulip is a garden plant, beautiful but scentless. One cannot make coffee on an infernal machine."

Mrs Goldhead: "*In gremio matris sedet sapientia patris.*[96] It's the same with the tulip. It has a bulb under the ground. Thus it is a bulbiferous plant."

Mr Goldhead: "Epileptics keep falling from the trees here. They are lured by the blue whistling of giant siphons. The image of the sacrosanct trinity glows above the alphabet tree. Are you not astonished, Mrs Goldhead, at the enormous childishness of everything?"

Mrs Goldhead: "Oh you and your fanatical high-flying ideas! We are dancing animals with towering headwear. We tussle with sobriety. Truly in vain. Who knows anything about anyone?"

Mr Goldhead: "Yes, but do you recall Sambuco?[97] Five houses on a green wall. The ground on which you are standing here: triangular shards of glass in outer space. Koko, the Green God, has bewitched us."

Mrs Goldhead: "Koko — do you mean our son? Why do you want to play *weltschmerz*? Your distance and melancholy, your precocity and experience: just think! Mouth, forehead and eye sockets buried in saffron. What are you complaining about?"

Strophe

Koko, the Green God, once soared in liberty
Above the market square in the kingdom of Sambuco.
But then he was caught and placed behind bars of coarse wire,
And fed with pomade and the petticoats of old maids.[98]
He made no reply to the mocking questions about his well-being.
He no longer prophesied the fates of the next world and its successor
Sat sad and forlorn on his wooden post.
The blessings he brought have ceased to abound.
His face shrivelled to that of an old trout
And he led a completely logical existence full of torpor.
Shaken at night by the madness conjured by the stars
He avenged himself by bewitching those closest to himself.

Antistrophe

The heinous light, shine out to him!
Sun of death, inflate the gables of the filthy Bumbu people who took him
prisoner.
His ballads are played on all the mouth-organs of modern times.
Upholstered streets are being prepared for his return.
The twelve signs of the zodiac can live from his fame.
The chief bigwig can spend the night with his sister-in-law as a reward.
People and animals discard the clothes of their bodies and woes,
When he returns from the custody of the bandy-legged robbers.

His mother has gone on a vendetta on his account in the here and beyond.
His father rocks the spirits of evil for him on his hand.
He has spurned us and erected living pictures from our torments.
He will break the spell which possesses us.

Mrs Goldhead: "May it come to pass."

Mr Goldhead: "When Metatron[99] strides heavy-footed across the firmament."

Mrs Goldhead: "He will pick up the earth by the four corners and shake off the godless."

Mr Goldhead: "Calm yourself, Madame, if you please. Let us climb upon the brightly coloured donkey and ride off leisurely across the abyss."

Mrs Goldhead: "Just a moment, if you don't mind. So that I can clasp the sun, this septic ulcer, with the fire tongs and light his way to the elevated path."

Chorus Seraphicus[100]

The sum and total becomes history.
The *danse macabre* aspires to allegory.
The unprecedented — enters for all to see.
In garish light: depravity.

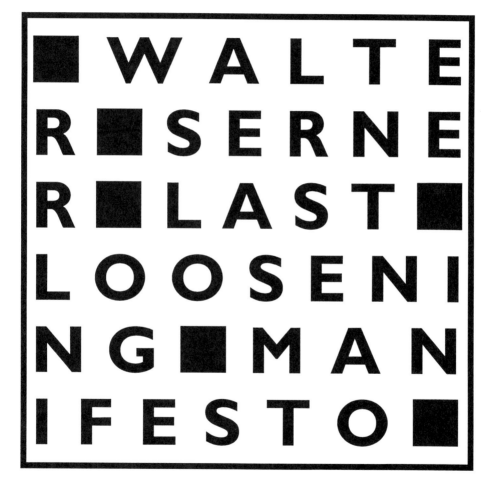

WALTE
RSERNE
RLAST
LOOSENI
NGMAN
IFESTO

151

Haeckel's attempts to solve the mystery of the universe were based on false premises and thus doomed to failure. Here is the sole possible
SOLUTION TO THE MYSTERY
OF THE UNIVERSE[101]

■**1.**

Racing around a fireball is a blob of filth on which ladies' silk stockings are sold and Gauguins prized. Truly a most deplorable business, yet one that nevertheless permits certain distinctions: silk stockings can be *grasped*, but not Gauguins. (Try to imagine Bernheim[103] as a prestigious biologist.) The thousand pea-brained *rastas* of the most *embêtant*[104] persuasion – who serve up columns of reviews to bourgeois index fingers in states of erection (O pastose toffs!) in order to unleash rivers of money – have to this end been responsible for such negligence that many a lady still ends up going short. (Here one should reflect for three minutes on the psychosis of poorly treated eyesight: clinical symptom, primary: underestimating silk stockings; secondary: digestive disorders.)

■**2.**

What did the first brain to find itself on this planet do? Presumably it was astonished at being here and hadn't a clue what to make of itself and the filthy vehicle beneath its feet. In the meantime people have come to terms with their brains by regarding them as so unimportant as to be not even worth ignoring, by making *rastas* of themselves (bottommost: blackish pole; uppermost: the president of the senate, say) and by turning the so-unjustly beloved nature into the backdrop for a right farce. Although this doubtless not especially heroic way of avoiding a dilemma that still receives insufficient appreciation has become quite void of any charm now that it is so utterly predictable (how infantile bathroom scales are!), for this self-same reason it is, however, highly suitable for conducting certain procedures.

■3.

Even an engine driver realises at least once a year that his relations with the locomotive are anything but binding and that he knows little more now about his spouse than he did after that balmy night in the Bois. (If I had said La Villette or Theresienwiese, the two relationships would have been quite illusory. A tip for budding professors: "On topographical anatomy, psychic changes of air and related matters.") In the Ronceroy Hotel or in Piccadilly, on the other hand, you may already find that it becomes damned unclear why now, of all times, you are gaping at your hand and carolling, hear yourself scratching and love your own spittle. This ever so peaceful example, or so it might appear, is the biggest opportunity for that importunate feeling of boredom to somersault its way up and become a thought considering its own cause. Lovely moments of this kind set up the desperado (my what a sweety!) who creates all sorts of mischief as a prophet, artist, anarchist, statesman etc., in short as a *rasta*.

■4.

Napoleon, who really was a sterling fellow, maintained quite irresponsibly that mankind's real calling is to till the soil. Why? Did the plough fall from heaven? But homo sapiens did manage to get a clue about SOMETHING, the voice of a lady undernourished by love I presume. Well, certainly not the soil; and when all is said and done, herbs and fruits existed already in those days. (Please consult the German biogeneticists here to discover why I am incorrect. But it will prove very boring. Consequently I am correct.) So in the end even Napoleon, who otherwise expressed himself with a delightfully refreshing lack of constraint, was from time to time an athlete in the field of the emotions. A shame. A real shame.

■5.

You see EVERYTHING is *rastaquouèresque*, my dear friends. Everyone is a (more or less) very flighty entity, *dieu merci*. (By the way: all credit to the industrious fellow who proves to me that there is anything that does NOT in the end rush about arbitrarily as a norm!) Otherwise, it should be added, death would become epidemic. Diagnosis: rampant boredom; or: panicky resignation; or: transcendental resentment, etc. (Continued *ad libitum*, this can be elevated to the register of all ungifted states.) The current state budget on the inhabited surface of the earth is thus merely the consequential result of boredom that has grown unbearable. Boredom: just to give its most inoffensive name! May each seek the most palatable word for his inferiority! (A dear little subject for a fierce game of forfeits!)

■6.

It is generally known that a dog is not a hammock; less so that failing to accept this tender hypothesis would cause the painters' daubing fists to slump at their sides; and completely unknown that interjections are far more apt: world views are word mixtures . . . *Sapristi*, the procedure must be slightly expanded here. (Small image: a gentle craniotomy!) So: all stylists are not even donkeys. Because style is merely a gesture of embarrassment with the wildest structure. And since embarrassment (after sleeping on it briefly) reveals itself as the most perfect self-regret, it is evident that stylists, fearing they will be mistaken for donkeys, behave far worse than them. (Donkeys you see have two quite outstanding characteristics: they are stubborn, and lazy.) Thus the difference between Paul Oskar Höcker, Dostoevsky, Roda-Roda and Wedekind[105] reveals itself solely in the restraint shown with regard to the aforementioned gesture of embarrassment. Whether someone purrs to me in perfectly functioning trochees or otherwise in a manner bristling with images (all images are plausible!) or in a naturalistic fashion, as it were, saying that he had felt sick, but that after he had seen it in black and white he felt better, or that he had in fact felt fine all along (hullo hullo!), but then became sick when he no longer understood it at all *(teremtete!)*: it's all just the same sub-donkey-like effort, the desire to escape one's embarrassment by giving it (stylistic, ogodogodo) form. Dreadful word! Which is to say: to make something that is probable out of life, which is improbable to the tips of its toes! To clap a redeeming heaven over this chaos of filth and enigma! To perfume and order this pile of human excrement! Thank's a lot! . . . Is there a more idiotic picture than an (ugh!) ingenious stylising mind playing the coquette with itself during this activity? (By the way: tuppence to the plucky fellow who proves to me that this coquettishness is NOT present among all the ethico-blusterers!) O, that frightfully cheerful embarrassment that ends with a bow before one's own self! THAT'S the reason (on account of this stylised curvature) why philosophies and novels are sweated out of people's pores, pictures are daubed, sculptures hewn, symphonies groaned out and religions founded. What appalling ambition, especially because these vain asinine games (i.e. especially in the German regions) have come to a complete nought. Nothing but horseplay!

■7.

The most beautiful landscape I know is the Café Barratte in Les Halles. For two reasons. It was there that I became acquainted with Germaine, who whispered, among other things: *"C'est possible que je serais bonne, si je saurais pourquoi."* I admit maliciously that I paled with pleasure. And secondly because in this friendly bar Jean Kartopaïtès, who otherwise only consorted with men without stiff collars, broke off relations with me brusquely because I was careless enough to drop the name Picasso.

■8.

Oh the darling white porcelain plates! Because . . . Well because: previously people wanted to convey what they claimed to be inexpressible, or in reality did not have, through painting. (Yippee! As if one could only make a neat and tidy portrait of a vice-queen if one didn't know that she was not an armchair! See: hammock!) Consequently one could smirk long in advance at the fix these smearers would end up in once they ceased jerking off oil-photos. (Behind their ears: more girls, please, more girls!) But the impressions! So: WHAT is achieved when, after blinking furiously, one manages to arrange things so that that potato gobbler also beholds only a cow, but was first able to puff himself up like THAT in the opinion it was HIS cow, a highly special cow, in short: THE one and only AND redeeming cow? *(teremtete!)* But the expressions! Ho ho: WHAT is achieved when one looks fixedly at what an adjective can accomplish because, having also failed until now to act as any sort of guide, it would already be a failure before it came to be painted? But the Cubists, the Futurists! Whoops: although the champions of these thoroughly ultra-violet failures of paint-brush-charges heralded that they would descend — like the *liberatio* (ugh!) — from the high swing of style (Charge of the trapeze! Charge of the trapeze! Roughly as follows: "We'll manage to get the swing of this embarrassment!"), all that they achieved was that not even a chignon began to swing, and worse still that the wildest donkeys arrived in the world at a steady trot. (O Sagot,[107] mounted by his brood! etc. etc.) Horseplay! Horseplay!

■9.

Basically a repetition of what has already been said in section 8 for those who have been brought up badly: an abecedarian matter, perfectly abecedarian! But to be noted anyway out of caution, my dearest:

a) Sculpture: highly unwieldy playthings, heightened by a metaphysical upward gaze.

b) Music: ersatz for Pantopon[108] or Eros. (Long since sub-abecedarian!).

c) Poetry: a young lad finds himself in a jam. Recipe: ask him who he dreams of and you can tell him with whom he has not slept.[109] (Naturally one is ALWAYS in a jam; but then one should no longer find oneself in the 'c' jam.)

d) Novels and so on: the goodly gentlemen talk as if they were being roasted on a spit, or more recently not at all. Just a bit more sweat and it will turn out well: *belles-lettres!* (One finds oneself on the spit rather often. But a volume from Samuel Fischer's[110] is a much too time-consuming method of creating the Syracuse-Sandwich-Central Heating airline.)

All in all, my dearest: art was a teething problem.

■ 10.

one never has a thought. At best the thought acts as if. (But there are always those who quibble about it!) Every word is a disgrace, mark you! People simply keep trumpeting out sentences with the most circus-like verve across a chain bridge (or even: ravines, plants, beds). Helpful suggestion: before falling asleep imagine with the greatest clarity the terminal mental state of a suicide who at last wishes to plumb the depths of self-awareness with a bullet. But you will only succeed if you have first made yourself ridiculous. Highly ridiculous. Terribly ridiculous. Ridiculous beyond all measure. So appallingly ridiculous that everything becomes equally ridiculous. That everyone falls metaphorically on his backside. And sneezes.

■ 11.

Interjections are the most fitting. (Oh the darling white porcelain plates!) . . . These amphibians and newts, who consider themselves too good to be donkeys, must be brought to reason by driving it out of them! Whipping it out of them! This ghastly, larger-than-life postcard-blue, which these dismal *rastas* have lied to high ha- ho- hi- hu- (pardon me?) heaven, must be torn down! One must tap one's head, carefully but firmly, on one's neighbour's as if on a rotten egg (good, good). One must bellow the utterly indescribable, the totally inexpressible, so unbearably close up that no dog would wish to continue leading its life so smartly — but rather far more stupidly! So that everyone loses their wits and gets their head back again! The pancakes, the Bible sayings, the girls' bosoms, the percentages, the Gauguins, the snot-rags, the stocking garters, the spirits, the lavatory seats, the waistcoats, the bugs — all the stuff that simultaneously they do, think of and pore over — must be shoved, one after another, so sharply in front of the curve of their chins until finally their feeling of well-being is as great as the mere feeling of woosiness they had experienced until then. One must. One simply must. *Teremtete!*

■12.

Silk stockings are priceless. A vice-queen IS an armchair. World views are word mixtures. A dog IS a hammock. *L'art est mort.* Viva Dada!

■NOTES

■INTRODUCTION

1. A broader introduction to the developments of Zurich Dada, particularly regarding such major protagonists as Hans Arp, Tristan Tzara and Hans Richter, who are not included in this anthology, can be found in the introduction to *The Dada Almanac*, Richard Huelsenbeck (ed.), Atlas Press, London, 1993.

2. See, for instance, Theodor Adorno, *Ästhetische Theorie*, Frankfurt am Main, 1970.

3. *Die Flucht aus der Zeit*, Munich and Leipzig, 1927, English translation, Viking Press, New York, 1967. All textual references in the text are henceforth given as: *Diary*.

4. The first four chapters were published separately in the magazine *Der Opal* in 1907 under the title *Herr Giorgio Bebuquin*.

5. *Über den Roman*, printed in *Die Aktion*, 1912.

6. Ha Hu Baley's sonnet *Baley's Love Song to Euphemia* is clearly dedicated to Einstein; Euphemia is the main female protagonist in *Bebuquin*.

7. The word *Bruitism* came originally from Luigi Russolo's Futurist manifesto *Noise Art*, 1913.

8. Such as the introduction to the *Dada Almanac*, q.v.

9. The first two publications being Tzara's *La première aventure céleste de M. Antipyrine* and Huelsenbeck's poem *Schalabei, Schalamezomai*.

10. Afterword to Huelsenbeck's *Phantastische Gebete* (reprint), Giessen, 1993.

11. Christian Schad, *Relative Realitäten*, in Walter Serner, *Die Tigerin*, Munich, 1971.

12. As mooted by Thomas Milch, the editor of his complete works (*Das Gesamte Werk*, Munich and Erlangen, 1979-1984), and Raoul Schrott, *Walter Serner und Dada*, Siegen,

1989, respectively.

13. The *Last Loosening Manifesto* published in this anthology constitutes, with minimal changes, the first section of this much lengthier manifesto. In addition a third, revised version, extended to full book length but with all references to Dada expunged, appeared in Hanover in 1927 with the subtitle *A handbook for conmen and those who wish to become such.*

14. Schrott, ibid.

15. *Dada Profile*, Zurich, 1961.

16. *Literarische Avantegarde und Dandysmus*, Frankfurt am Main, 1989

17. This reading of the chapter is propounded by Claudia Rechner-Zimmermann, in *Die Flucht in die Sprache*, Marburg 1992.

18. These include a paraphrase of the words "if you've seen one phallus you've seen them all"; a description of the Devil wearing a *cul de Paris*; Ball's remarks on a publication by Ludwig Rubiner; and references to the *Saurapuranam*, a compendium of Sivaism.

19. An expression coined by the writer and publicist Kurt Hiller, in *Die Weisheit der Langeweile* (*The Wisdom of Boredom*), 1913. The cortex is also an important symbol in Benn's play.

20. From Ball's essay *Byzantine Christianity*, 1923.

21 A book which also influenced Huysmans and Jarry among others.

■FANTASTIC PRAYERS

The poems on pages 76 to 84 only appeared in the second, extended edition of *Fantastic Prayers,* published in Berlin in 1920. The version of *Blissful Rhythms* on page 72 appeared only in the first edition (Zurich 1916). The eccentric use of capitals has been adhered to in this translation. The "meaningless" Bruitist words in the original have been modified where sense dictated for English pronunciation.

22. **Schickaneder**, Emanuel (1751-1812): librettist and theatre director who also wrote the text to Mozart's *The Magic Flute*.

23. **Rataplan**: English in the original, meaning a tattoo beaten on a drum.

24. **Umba da umba**: "My negro poems all ended with the refrain 'Umba, umba,' which I kept roaring at the audience with enormous pathos." (Richard Huelsenbeck, *Mit Witz, Licht und Grütze*, 1957).

25. **Mpala tano/trou-ouserfly**: In this poem as in the others, the translator has kept to the first edition, ignoring the minimal differences with the later Berlin edition. Here it is perhaps worth mentioning though the stresses given in the later version: Mpala tanó and eloé.

26. **Mafarka the Futurist**: Title of a novel by the Futurist poet Filippo Marinetti.

27. **Ludwig the Coquette**: An acquaintance from Huelsenbeck's years in Berlin. In *En Avant Dada* (1920), Huelsenbeck describes his and Hugo Ball's feeling of disgust on reading the reviews of their Expressionist Evening in 1915: "We decided to put an end to our lives with drink. We entered one of the more or less secret brothels in Potsdamerstraße where we met the coquette Ludwig. But on that evening she was simply intent on masochism, just for business reasons, which suited neither us nor our programme."

28. **Watch on the Rhine**: seriously patriotic song, dating from the French invasion of the Rhine region.

29. **Hans Kasiske**: Huelsenbecks' former brother-in-law, and friend in Berlin.

30. **Cnuckabout**: The translator was unable to trace this word, perhaps the English "knockabout?"

31. **Teremtete**: Hungarian argot expression, roughly "Hell's bells."

32. **Dadasopher**: The Dada name of Raoul Hausmann (1886-1971), a major protagonist in Berlin.

33. **Hohenfriedberger**: Military march, celebrating Friedrich II of Prussia's spectacular defeat of the vastly superior Austro-Silesian troops in 1745.

34. **Dadaco (Dadako)** was planned by Huelsenbeck and Tzara as the "Dada Hand Atlas" or "Universal Atlas," a vast international compilation of Dada texts, manifestos, poems and pictures with typographic layout by John Heartfield. Unfortunately the publisher, Kurt Wolff, was less than enamoured by the contents and the soaring prices, and pulled out. All that remained were 13 trial sheets and a large bill for Wolff. Much of its written contents appeared, however, in the *Dada Almanac*.

35. **The End of the World**: a paraphrase of *Weltende,* the title of a renowned early Expressionist poem of the absurdist persuasion by Jakob van Hoddis (1887-1942).

36. **Monist Society**: followers of Ernst Haeckel (1834-1919), whose philosophy of Monism attempted to unite religion and Darwinism.

37. **Friedrich Ebert** (1871-1925): first Reichspresident of the Weimar government in Germany, who was co-responsible for sending in mercenaries to slaughter the revolutionaries in Berlin in March 1919.

38. **Abba**: an honorific for 'father' in many Semitic languages.

■TENDERENDA THE FANTAST

39. **Saint Bernard**: Abbot of Clairvaux (1090-1153), whom Ball discovered in an anthology of mystic poets of the middle ages, *Le Latin mystique*, edited by Remy de Gourmont and prefaced by J-K.Huysmans. The legend, written by St. Bernard for his own tomb, reads:

Oh you, my ladies and gentlemen
who look upon this painting,
please pray for the souls
of those buried therein.

40. **The prophet strode with violet face**: an interesting parallel can be found in a line of the poem *The Blue Evening* (*Der blaue Abend*) written by Ball and Hans Leybold under the pseudonym Ha Hu Baley: "Enchanted a violet prophet floated away from the people."

41. **Big Chief Fireshine**: in Ball's autobiographical novel *Flametti*, the title figure, a vaudeville impresario who is a passionate fire-eater, stages a Red Indian musical spectacle in which he plays the lead role of "Chief Fireshine." The impresario is portrayed as a man of uncomplicated, earthy dynamism.

42. **Benjamin**: this figure is probably Ball's homage to the similarly named title figure of Carl Einstein's novella *Bebuquin, the Dilettantes of the Miracle,* which influenced him considerably. The epigrammatic style is very similar, and both texts underline their authors' battles against the destruction of language and its subservience to expediency.

43. **Shoe polish**: in his diary, 25.11.1914, Ball wrote: "Today I saw a brand of shoe polish bearing the legend 'The thing in itself.' "

44. **Watch on the Rhine**: cf. footnote 28.

45. **Denmark**: another level of association in the figure of Johann is evident from the fact that in early 1916 Emmy Hennings' daughter Anne-Marie was brought to Switzerland for safe-keeping. Emmy Hennings came from Flensburg near the Danish border, and her daughter was nicknamed "Sea-horse."

46. **The Blue Tulip**: the name echoes the 'Blue Flower' of Romanticism and the 'Blue Rider' Expressionist group.

47. **Swaggerprance**: this portrait of an extreme Bohemian poet who, "sickening from inexplicable and unmistakable depressions, falls apart amidst nervous spasms and paralysis" (*Flight out of Time*) suggests that Swaggerprance is based loosely on Stanislav Przybyszewski (1868-1927), high-priest of the Berlin Decadents, whom Ball met in 1913. This surmise is given some support by the fact that his wife was named Dagny, as is a character who appears in this chapter. The Expressionist poet Ferdinand Hardekopf described him as follows: "O I love him . . . his terrible fatalism, his mediaeval blazing, the

pathos of his addiction to destruction and his fear, his primal, eternal fear of life and death!"

48. **A captain**: the original word *Hauptmann* not only means "captain," but is also the name of the naturalist author Gerhart Hauptmann (1862-1946), who wrote *Die Insel der großen Mutter* (*The Island of the Great Mother*).

49. **Lilienstein**: in Ball's *First Dada Manifesto* (delivered in Zurich, 14.7.1916) he mentions one Anastasius Lilienstein in the same breath as the Expressionist writer and publicist Ludwig Rubiner and the Swiss arts correspondent Korrodi. Here Lilienstein would seem to contain one of Ball's alter-egos.

50. **Kis de Paris**: possibly a play on words on the French word for bustle, *cul de Paris*, because Ball in his diary mentions an image of the Devil who appears as a contented old maid wearing a *cul de Paris*. *Ridicule* in this context would thus be the French slang for *réticule* or handbag.

51. **Matat**: presumably Marat, Dadaised by a typing error.

52. **Qui hic...**: "Whoever here hath pissed or shat / May he feel the wrath of the gods of heaven and hell."

53. **Scheblimini**: this word has resisted both discovery and informed guesswork. The Latin is: "He sitteth by my right hand."

54. **Petroleum**: once again the real life model for Big Chief Fireshine (cf. note 41). In his diary (3/10/1915) Ball comments that the impresario ". . . has a bad stomach because he has drunk too much petrol . . . in order to spit flames three metres long."

55. **Ludwig Rubiner** was a politically active Expressionist who was acquainted with Ball in Zurich, and whom Ball on several occasions attacked for championing the concept of the literati. The nearest Rubiner came to writing such a handbook was a set of "Criminal sonnets" composed with two friends in 1913. Ball, however, seems to be playing with associations here: in 1898 a famous *Handbook of Criminal Psychology* was published by Hans Groß. His son Otto became the *enfant terrible* of psychoanalysis. He preached and practised

anarchy, free love and drug use to liberate the Id, and was also active in Expressionist circles; he was later cast into a series of mental hospitals by his father on the pretext of schizophrenia. The campaign for Otto Groß's release became an international *cause célèbre* among the avant-garde: there were fiery protests in the Expressionist magazine *Die Aktion,* and issue 5 of *Revolution,* an Expressionist periodical co-edited by Ball, was dedicated to Otto Groß's release, and contained articles from Cendrars, Huelsenbeck and Rubiner amongst others. Rubiner's contribution is all the more intriguing in that he had previously rejected Groß's writing and psychoanalysis as a whole. Thus in typical fashion Ball, who may well have known Groß personally, would appear to have collaged the pursued Groß into the character Lilienstein.

56. **Zackopadores**: the translator has been unable to identify this animal.

57. **No connection with the action**: a sly reference to *Die Aktion,* and to the announcement by its editor, Franz Pfemfert, in 1915, that Ball "has no connections with *Die Aktion*" after Ball attacked the magazine for preaching nihilism and utilitarian mass politics during a discussion on the Russian Revolution.

58. **Soxlet apparatus**: an extraction apparatus invented by Franz Soxhlet (1848-1926); **Autolax** was a proprietary brand of laxative.

59. **Devil-painter**: the Tyrolean dialect word *Tuifelmaler* refers to a rural artisan who decorates the crosses on graves, wardrobes etc.

60. **Erich Ludendorff**: Prussian field-marshal who commanded alongside Hindenburg during the First World War in true sabre-rattling fashion.

61. **Rachitic populace**: besides attributes clearly linked with machines and the war, the following characters would seem to contain features of various Expressionists: P.T. Bridet has touches of Gottfried Benn, writer of a celebrated cycle of gruesome poems entitled *Morgue,* although the name Bridet comes from the first agronomist to recycle excrement; Pimperling refers more overtly to Theodor Däubler, the writer of the epic poem *Northern Lights;* and Toto to Albert Ehrenstein, whose famous novel *Tubutsch* ends with "I've nothing except for — my name."

62. **Poisonous smile**: the original pun resists any exact rendering: the German word *Giftlache* suggests a poisonous laugh or a puddle of poison, but also means cheap booze and, figuratively, cheap prose.

63. **Jericho stomacher**: *Jerichobinde* is the name of a Zurich bar in Ball's earlier novel *Flametti*, rather appropriately since Jericho is in both English and German a humorous term for a "quiet place." Here the curious name has been taken literally.

64. **Hespar, salfurio...**: in an essay entitled *Berthold Schwarz, the Inventor of Gunpowder* (1915), Ball gives a similar list as the contents of Grecian Fire: "naphtha, bitumen, brimstone and succinite."

65. **Umbala**: *the* Dada word used in their fake Negro poetry, coined by Richard Huelsenbeck.

66. **Corpse about thy head**: Ball's diary entry of 3/7/1915 relates that he was given a compendium of Sivaism, the *Saurapuranam*, from which he quotes: "Siva lives in the fields of corpses and wears a garland of corpses around his head." Ball draws on this book on several occasions in *Tenderenda*.

67. **A small Jewish boy**: not inconceivably Tristan Tzara.

68. **Plimplamplasko**: eponymous hero of the book by Friedrich Klinger (1752-1831), a satire on the amorality and antisocial attitudes of self-proclaimed genius, and Rousseau's notion of the inherent goodness of man. This latter notion is one which Ball frequently considers in his diaries. Ball intended using the title for a collection of his poems that never appeared.

69. **The roast poet** refers to Baudelaire's *Fusées*, in which he writes: "everyone would be utterly astonished if a poet asked the state for the right to keep a few members of the middle-classes in his stables, but it would be considered completely natural if someone from the middle-classes ordered roast poet."

70. **In Germano...**: "In Germany all is flux."

71. **The philosophy of "as if"** or fictionalism was founded by Hans Vaihinger (1852-1933): a form of pragmatism based on Kant's *Principle of Pure Reason*, it was instrumental in undermining certainty in scientific statement.

72. **Mea res...**: "My duty is to act"

73. **Satana...**: paraphrase of "O salute, O Satana / O Ribellione," the first line of a famous poem by Giosué Carducci (1861-1901) which became the rallying cry of the 19th century Italian free-thinkers and revolutionaries.

74. **Psychofact**: in Ball's obituary (*Totenrede*, 1915) of his fallen friend Hans Leybold (1892-1914), he refers to their jointly written proto-Dada poems which were published under the name Ha-Hu Baley as follows: "we placed a psychofact in the world which we called Baley, and which had the aim of cultivating poses, gestures and vexations." The obituary in this chapter seems likewise to be directed to Leybold.

75. **Max Reinhardt**: the irony of this reference becomes clear when one reads that Ball and fellow Expressionist and later Dadaist Richard Huelsenbeck fought in vain against this famous theatre director's depoliticization of the *Freie Volksbühne* theatre in Munich. Leybold, who supported Ball's theatrical plans, would doubtless have agreed.

76. **Salvarsan**: a treatment for syphilis, notorious for its side effects, invented by P. Ehrlich in 1910.

77. **The Putrefaction Conductor**: the original title of this chapter (*Der Verwesungsdirigent*), written in 1919, is almost identical with that of a short play by Gottfried Benn, published in the same year, entitled *Der Vermessungsdirigent* ("The Measurement Conductor"). Benn's wonderfully grotesque "epistemological drama" revolves around his typical theme of the Apollonian and Dionysian poles of knowledge and intoxication, the first pole typified by a tragic gynaecologist whose incisive intellectual drive and logic becomes totally self-destructive and leads to the collapse of his own ego; he "measures everything, hence, measurement conductor" (Benn, 1934), steadily rejecting his cultural and philosophical heritage to leave nothing but an imaginary point of reference to the world, an "Archimedean point." The other protagonist is the painter Picasso who, at first sick and

entangled in his "cerebrum," later develops into a sensual and self-creative person unhindered by the intellect. At this point Picasso, who until then had also been an "Archimedean point," hurls the curious insult "measurement conductor" at the doctor after the latter has praised the cold, static glory of a set of marble stairs, symbol of clarity and respite from intellectual despair. Ball's shift in emphasis is only marginal, given his view that the "measuring, weighing and counting" logical rationalism introduced by Kant abstracts thought from things, and thenceforth enslaves the objects of this world to reason and control. Objects become denigrated matter or putrefaction which can be 'conducted.'

Ball and Benn were acquainted in Germany before Ball started to write *Tenderenda*; they shared an interest in Nietzsche, an admiration for Einstein's *Bebuquin*, a linguistic scepticism combined with a feeling for a deeper or rhythmic reality in language once freed from the functional slavery of the intellect, and their initial dandyism. It would also be surprising if Ball hadn't found something close to his heart in the black slapstick of Benn's play, and we find several obscure references to this work in this chapter (e.g. the "Buxom Leg" club's measureing machines, or the reference to the naked (=Archimedean) point, and elsewhere.

78. **Washing machine of banalisation**: in his diary (20/9/1916), Ball refers to the Press as the "mills of banalisation" driven by wind and water.

79. **Tahure**: *La Butte de Tahure* was the scene of a violent battle in Marne, France, in 1915. By adding hyphens, Ball has changed the word to "Ta-who-re." The association of the "harlot war" is strengthened by a brief passage in his earlier novel *Flametti*, where he gives laconic mention to an amusement at a Bern funfair: a panopticon of the battle entitled "Tahure, the fiery cauldron."

80. **Gleim**, Johann Wilhelm (1719-1803), writer of patriotic Prussian songs glorifying war and victory.

81. **Abdulhamid II** (1842-1918), autocratic Ottoman sultan who forced the reform movement according to Western models.

82. **Jolifanto...**: although Ball described his *Lautgedichte* (sound poems) in his diary: "I let the vowels perform somersaults. I simply allow the sounds to come forth, just as a cat miaows . . .," an underlying sense can be found in this poem, which reads in German like Lewis Carroll's *Jabberwocky*. An English version might start as follows:

Joliphanto bambla ô falli bambla
biggerli muncha haveri herd
égiga goramen
higo bloiko trunkla yupyup
etc.

and such words as zunbatha, watabatha, kissa gummsa etc. are fairly unmistakable.

83. **Laurentius-tears**: originally *Laurentius-Tränen*, the popular German name for the Pleiades. Legend tells that on St. Lawrence's death, the sky was lit by shooting stars.

84. **Tower of thy Grace**: of all the many towers that appear in this novel, this one is identifiable as that of Wittenberg Cloister, in which Luther received his inspiration that justness can come only from God's grace.

85. **St. Ambrosius . . .**: on concluding *Tenderenda*, Ball wrote in his diary: "May all those attacks of wickedness lie buried inside it, of which Saint Ambrosius says:

Procul recedant somnia
Et noctium phantasmata,
Hostemque nostrum conprime . . . "

(May dreams withdraw to far away / And the spectres of the night / Oppress also our enemy)

Later, in an essay entitled *The Artist and the Malaise of the Times*, Ball wrote "the demonic phantasms mentioned by Saint Ambrose come from the individual and phylogenetic store of images within the imagination."

86. **Prayer book manufacturer**: i.e. Richard Huelsenbeck, author of the *Fantastic Prayers*.

87. **Elomen**: an enticing, unidentifiable sigil also to be found in Ball's *Lautgedicht* "*Wolken*" "Clouds."

88. **The Blue Rider** was the name adopted by the early Expressionist group of painters around Kandinsky; the Red Bikers (*Rote Radler*) is a German courier company, originally employing cyclists who wore red jackets and caps.

89. **Cui bono**: "What good would it do?"

90. **Benedicat...**: "May he bless Tenderenda, O Lord, and keep thee from all the tricks of the Devil."

91. **Quelle fleur tenez-vous dans le bec**: "What is that flower you are holding in your beak?" a line from a simultaneous poem by Huelsenbeck and Tzara, "*Dialogue entre un cocher et une allouette*," published in *Cabaret Voltaire* in 1916. The reply is:

"It is your talent which people say is excellent / at the moment lark shit / what is that flower you are holding in your beak? / And you constantly go "*pette*" [fart] like a German poet."

92. **Sedia gestatoria**: the papal litter used for festive processions.

93. **Baubo...**: again, the cats and peacocks can be recognised in this poem. "Faffa" and "Fafâmo" resemble the German word *Pfau* for peacock; the cat's mewing is given in the word "mjâma."

94. **Music-stands...**: Hugo Ball's famous recitations at the Dada evenings were performed using music-stands to support the texts.

95. **Koko the Green God** first appeared in the opening verse of Hugo Ball's poem *Cabaret*, published in 1916 in the periodical *Cabaret Voltaire*:

"The exhibitionist places himself, legs astride, before the curtain
and Pimpronella entices him with her red petticoats.
Koko the Green God applauds loudly in the audience.
Even the oldest scapegoats get randy."

Koko was also the nickname of the painter Oskar Kokoschka whose eccentric play *Sphinx and Strawman* was performed at the Galerie Dada in 1917. Ball had intended enlisting his help for his Expressionistic theatre in 1914.

96. **In gremio...**: "The wisdom of the father lies in the lap of the mother."

97. **Sambuco**: a small valley with a lake in Tessin which Emmy Hennings and Hugo Ball enthused about after a visit in 1919 ("an emerald dream" — Ball in his diary).

98. **Petticoats of old maids**: the fact that Koko was captivated by the sight of petticoats in the poem entitled *Cabaret* mentioned above (see note 95), plus the fact that he was held prisoner by "the filthy Bumbu people," who sound like those self-styled 'primitives' the Dadaists, suggests that Koko is still held captive by the Dadas.

99. **Metatron**: a supreme angelic being in Jewish Gnosticism.

100. **Chorus Seraphicus**: this is a disrespectful paraphrase of the *Chorus Mysticus* at the conclusion of Goethe's *Faust* Part 2.

■ LAST LOOSENING MANIFESTO

101. **Haeckel's attempts...**: This quotation comes from the advertising band around the extended version of the manifesto, entitled *Last Loosening Manifesto Dada*, published in Hannover, 1920. (See note 36 for Ernst Haeckel.)

102. **Hoboken**: Anton van (1887-1983), wealthy Dutchman who was a friend of Serner's in Switzerland, and probably backed him financially.

103. **Bernheim**: Alexandre (1839-1915) Parisian gallery owner and publisher who exhibited the Impressionists and Expressionists.

104. *Embêtant*: French for "annoying."

105. **Höcker**: Paul Oskar (1865-1944), author of numerous novels and plays; **Roda-Roda**: pseudonym of Sándor Rosenfeld (1872-1945), Austrian humorist, journalist and

cabarettist; **Wedekind**: Frank (1864-1918), rumbustious playwright of the anti-bourgeois persuasion.

106. **Sagot**: Edouard, Parisian publisher and art dealer.

107. **Pantopon**: ersatz drug for opium or morphine.

108. **Ask him who he dreams of . . .**: here Serner is parodying Ludwig Rubiner's essay *Psychoanalysis*, published in 1913 in *Die Aktion*: "The apothecary's method: tell me who you dreamt of and I shall tell you with whom you have not slept. An excellent method."

109. **Samuel Fischer's**: renowned German publishing house that produced much of the better fiction of its day.

■ RELATED TITLES FROM ATLAS PRESS

THE DADA ALMANAC. Edited by Richard Huelsenbeck, Berlin, 1920. Introduced and annotated by Malcolm Green & Alastair Brotchie. Translated by Malcolm Green, Barbara Wright, Terry Hale & Derk Wynand. Illustrations, biographies, etc, 176 pp. £12.99. (In print.)

THE DADA ALMANAC was assembled by Richard Huelsenbeck, one of the foremost Dadaists from the very inception of Dada to its end, and published in Berlin in 1920 at the high-point of Dadaist activities in the German capital: the Dada Almanac was and is the most important single Dadaist publication. Containing a wide range of poetry, polemics, essays, manifestos and deliberate confusions, not only does it present the vast range of Dadaist literary production and experimentation on an international scale, it also reveals many of the apparent contradictions which lie at the heart of Dada. Between rallying cries for abstract art and calls for a return to objectiveness, between political commitment and naughty pranks, insult and high art, atheism and mysticism, and much much more, the Dada Almanac shows the vital paradoxes which have surrounded Dada with so much of its mystique. As such the Dada Almanac is an essential document for anyone who wishes to reassess the often two-dimensional image which Dada has been bequeathed by the Parisian section of the movement.

Authors: Hans Arp, Johannes Baader, Hugo Ball, Paul Citröen, Paul Dermée, Daimonides, Max Goth, John Heartfield, Raoul Hausmann, Richard Huelsenbeck, Vincente Huidobro, Mario D'Arezzo, Adon Lacroix, Walter Mehring, Francis Picabia, Georges Ribemont-Dessaignes, Alexander Sesqui, Philippe Soupault, Tristan Tzara.

This annotated version of the Almanac, *the first to appear in English, is a crucial document for anyone interested in the history of the 20th century avant-garde.* —**The New York Times Book Review**. The Dada Almanac *is an excellent place to experience Dadaism in its own terms and in all its contradictions ... If there's a reason that the Dadaists appeal to our own cultural confusions, it can undoubtedly be discovered here.* —**Los Angeles Times.** *...still thrilling, still weird.* —**Artforum.**

(See over)

ARTHUR CRAVAN, JACQUES RIGAUT, JULIEN TORMA, JACQUES VACHÉ.
4 DADA SUICIDES, introductions by Roger Conover, Terry Hale & Paul Lenti, translations
by Terry Hale, Paul Lenti & Iain White, (Anti-classics 2), 270 pp, ISBN 0 947757 74 0.

This book collects together works by four "writers" on the fringes of the Dada movement
in 1920's Paris. These four took the nihilism of the movement to its ultimate conclusion,
their works being remnants of lives lived to the limit and then cast aside with nonchalance
and abandon: Vaché died of a drug overdose, Rigaut shot himself, Cravan and Torma
simply vanished, their fates still a mystery. Yet their fragmentary works — to which they
attached so little importance — still exert a powerful allure and were a vital inspiration for
the literary movements that followed them. Vaché's bitter humour, Cravan's energetic
invective, Rigaut's dandyfied introspection, and Torma's imperturbable asperity: all had
their influence.

The collection contains biographical introductions to each author as well as personal
recollections by their contemporaries.

Atlas has published texts from over 200 authors spanning the avant-garde anti-tradition of
the last one hundred years. Many titles are only available direct from the publisher. For a
free catalogue, write to:

BCM ATLAS PRESS, 27 OLD GLOUCESTER ST, LONDON WCIN 3XX.